THE LAMP AND THE BOOK

By the same Author

GERALD BOWMAN

THE LAMP AND THE BOOK

The story of the Rcn 1916–1966

THE QUEEN ANNE PRESS LIMITED

Published by The Queen Anne Press,
Gulf House, 2 Portman Street, London, W.1
and The Royal College of Nursing
and National Council of Nurses of the United Kingdom,
Henrietta Place, London, W.1
Printed in Great Britain by
Thomas Nelson (Printers) Ltd, London and Edinburgh

CONTENTS

LIST OF ILLUSTRATIONS

ACKNOWLEDGEMENTS

My sincere thanks are due to those members and staff of the Royal College of Nursing, and National Council of Nurses of the United Kingdom for all their help and assistance in the preparation of this book.

I also gratefully acknowledge the sources of a great part of the background material to this account, which I have drawn from many historians of the nursing profession, notably Lucy Ridgely Seymer's 'A General History of Nursing', Brian Abel-Smith's 'A History of the Nursing Profession', and Agnes E. Pavey's 'The Story of the Growth of Nursing'.

Finally I am glad of the opportunity to thank the Editor of *The Nursing Times* for the courtesy of allowing me access to that journal's files, and Miss Phyllis J. Court for work of most conscientious research.

G. B.

First Seeds

THE CIRCUMSTANCES which led to the foundation of the Royal College of Nursing were, to some extent, the result of indomitable striving for the betterment of nursing by Ethel Gordon Manson. Yet, paradoxically, she was not among the founders of the College, was never even a member and, indeed, fought against its declared principles when it was established. In tracing the history of nursing as it concerns the College foundation it is, however, necessary to pay full tribute to the campaign to raise nursing standards which Ethel Gordon Manson (later Mrs. Bedford Fenwick) led for sixty years of her dedicated but turbulent life. Her career even if judged by the standards of eighty-odd years ago was extraordinary.

Born on 26 January 1857, daughter of a wealthy doctor, she became a paying probationer at the Children's Hospital, Nottingham, in her teens and went on to take general training at the Royal Infirmary, Manchester. By the time she was twenty-one she was a sister at the London Hospital, and three years later was appointed Matron of St. Bartholomew's Hospital.

In that year, 1882, nursing was not considered a possible occupation for gentlewomen, although some who had entered it after the early death of husbands or sweethearts were 'understood' by their families and friends. The example of the great Florence Nightingale was, of course, well enough known to the world, but Florence had undertaken the nursing of wounded officers and their men in the Crimea. In such places as the Manchester Infirmary and 'Barts' poor people and even paupers were cared for, and there was no romantic background of battle and patriotism.

People of her own circle found Ethel Manson very difficult to understand. Her father died in her early life and her mother married again, this time a Member of Parliament in still wealthier circumstances, and the family's home was made at Thoroton Hall, Notts. Miss Manson, although not tall, was by then a beautiful girl in the statuesque way so admired of the period. She had her own comfortable means, she was well connected socially, and certainly showed a love of fine clothes —which remained with her for life. She could look forward to an existence of pleasure and gaiety and probably a brilliant marriage, yet she chose the dangers (then very real), the revolting sights, and general horrors of hospital life.

The reason why she did so was two-fold. First, the movement for the emancipation of women was making itself known, and secondly Ethel Manson had a good, well-educated mind, dynamic energy, and immovable stubbornness. Once she had decided that some principle or policy was right, no matter what happened to prove the opposite, she would not believe herself wrong, or anyway admit it. This trait was her Achilles heel in the really great work she did for nursing. Having worked and campaigned until she was generally the acknowledged leader of the nursing profession, she could not bring herself to admit that the founders of the College of Nursing or even Florence Nightingale were advancing far more practical and workable plans than her own.

She therefore fought Miss Nightingale's influence, which was far more powerful than hers. She agreed to negotiate with the College at its inception but later made co-operation impossible and finally broke away into open enmity. The results were, of course, pre-ordained.

Nevertheless, her personal achievements made her one of the most outstanding figures in the early history of nursing organization.

At the age of thirty in 1887, she married a prosperous and politically minded practitioner, Dr. Bedford Fenwick, and retired from active nursing. With typical energy, however, she founded in that year in her own drawing-room in Portland Place, the British Nurses Association of which she was voted permanent president. The object of the Association was to petition Parliament for a state register of two categories of nurses—nurses with three years' training and a certificate of good character, or educated ladies with only one year of training.

There were practical reasons beyond the obvious snobbery of this distinction. At that time, only women whose tone and pronunciation were not 'common' were likely to have received any education worth the name—in spite of the new State schools. At any rate they had been brought up by parents who believed in more civilized standards than that of the mass-average.

These standards, as much as actual education, were factors Ethel Bedford Fenwick held in the highest value. She hoped to recruit future nurses from 'a class of women who have been trusted for so many years that there will be few failures'.

On this point the already-legendary Florence Nightingale disagreed with her entirely. The ideal nursing-recruit in Miss Nightingale's opinion was a girl 'of the small farmer's daughter class', physically strong, endowed with solid common sense, energetic, and cheerful. She believed that the educational standard need be little more than an ability to read and write, and that a probationer nurse could learn in six months all that would be necessary for the rest of her professional life. In the conditions of that time she was right.

Naturally Florence Nightingale's views carried great influence in the corridors of power of the day, but there remained the undeniable fact that she herself had carefully recruited the pupils of her training school at St. Thomas's from ladies, most of whom had since become matrons of the greater hospitals.

On the broad view, however, her ideas were the more practical. Although both she and Ethel Bedford Fenwick were in the first rank of the movement for women's emancipation, they both knew that ladies of the period could earn their livings only as nurses, school-teachers, governesses, or companions without losing caste. But for the hard work, long hours, and often revolting details of nursing, dedication was a necessity. Florence Nightingale had first-hand experience of the proportion of girls from comfortable homes who had given up before completing training. There were, indeed, girls of any class who did the same, but the proportion was lower among those who were used to hard work and lacked, or could control, finer sensibilities. She had a biting contempt for any women who tried nursing for 'romantic' reasons, visualizing themselves in a saintly role but lacking the stamina or courage to meet practical conditions.

Ethel Bedford Fenwick was herself somewhat romantic in believing that there would be enough women from more fortunate homes who would stay the course and fulfil the ever growing demand for nurses. Later she was to modify her demands in this respect, but never to admit that had circumstances been ideal she was wrong.

She was a crusader of almost fanatical spirit, a close friend of Mrs. Pankhurst who was leading the campaign for the women's vote. She believed that only educated women could have a chance of winning freedom for womankind who were debarred from almost all professions and who, until 1882, five years beforehand, had had no legal right to their own money after marriage.

She wanted her own profession of nursing to be brought into the same category, if not on a level with, the profession of medicine. That was the object of her first proposed state register to be exclusive to those who were fully trained and could pass an examination demanding a high educational standard. Only those women were to bear the honoured title of Nurse.

For the rest, her original proposal was that those who could not or would not train and sit for the examination, no matter how long or how efficient they had been in practice, should drop the work.

CHAPTER TWO

The Nightingale Training School

THE GENERAL educational standard being what it was at that
time this principle would have meant that some 40,000 nurses
then practising would have had to give up, for Mrs. Bedford
Fenwick wanted only registered nurses to be legally allowed to
practise. Florence Nightingale's objections were practical and
clear: some hundred thousand nurses were needed as things
stood, and the demand would grow yearly with the increase in
population.

Ethel Bedford Fenwick, however, recruited 100 matrons,
100 doctors and 100 sisters or nurses for the council of her
British Nurses Association. She was also able to get Queen
Victoria's daughter, Princess Christian, to be Patron. This led
to the Association being granted a Royal Charter some six
years later, but internal stresses and strains developed. Under
the terms of the Association all officials had to be re-elected
every three years. Moreover the word 'register' was dropped
and 'list' substituted. This was largely through background
work by Florence Nightingale who believed that registration
would damage the profession of nursing by seeming to try and
bring it on a level with medicine. Already, she knew, many
doctors, especially in the provinces, were jealous of nurses
because, to save money, some people would call in nurses in
their stead. There was also friction in the fact that some nurses
came from an obviously higher social level than some doctors.
And finally she did not believe that a nurse's most important
qualities could be found by written examination. Undoubtedly
Miss Nightingale's views were well known in the R.B.N.A.
since several of her ex-pupils were matron members.

In 1892 Ethel Bedford Fenwick bought the *Nursing Record*
(which afterwards became the *British Journal of Nursing*) as a
vehicle in which to air her views. These were not always popular

with women senior to her in the profession and far more experienced, but who lacked her personal fortune. In its columns she fiercely attacked all and sundry who might oppose her, and later when she was at war with the College of Nursing her editorials became vitriolic.

However, her great abilities and energy show in the fact that she was the active Editor of the magazine for over fifty years, wrote for it regularly and also for the general press, and in 1910–11 received the deserved compliment of election as President of the Society of Women Journalists which she was asked to represent at the Coronation of King George V at Westminster Abbey; a matter which pleased her enormously and to which she would refer during the remainder of her life.

There is no doubt that in the early days her dominant spirit did not always make working with her congenial to those of a less self-assured turn. The outcome was that in 1894 she had the humiliation of being voted off the Council of the Royal British Nurses Association which she had formed. Her husband forthwith resigned from his position as treasurer. Registration was announced as dropped by the R.B.N.A. Almost everything they had jointly worked for came to nothing.

It may well be that she had not kept a tight enough personal hand upon R.B.N.A. affairs, because in 1893 she had gone off to America to attend the Chicago World Fair, in which there was a British Nurses Exhibit, organized by herself. The results were important in the history of nursing. Ethel Bedford Fenwick met the Superintendents of eighteen American nurse training schools, then patterned on Nightingale principles or those of the Kaiserwerth institution in Germany—disapproved of by Florence Nightingale, but which will be detailed a little later. The American women were deeply impressed by Mrs. Bedford Fenwick's ideas and as a result formed their own Society of Superintendents of Training Schools, giving honour to her name which still looms large in American nursing histories. More than this she met the then president of the International Council of Women, and was inspired to form in 1900 the International Council of Nurses on the same general lines.

Meanwhile, in 1894 she had formed the Matrons' Council of

Great Britain and Ireland, and in 1904 the National Council of Nurses to represent British nurses on the International Council.

However, things with the R.B.N.A. had never gone as hoped. It had no control over training schools and, in fact, did not stick rigidly by its own rules about the length of training required for entrants. It did not succeed in attracting a large membership at any time. It had, however, one item of inestimable value, its Royal charter granted in 1893. This was destined to be a strong negotiating point with the College of Nursing, but the College still lay in the future.

Ethel Bedford Fenwick's new campaign was immensely strengthened in 1902 by the passing of the Midwives Act, a result of Bills presented to Parliament since 1878. After this was law no woman could attend women in childbirth otherwise than under the direction of a qualified practitioner, unless she was certified under the Act. Certification and registration was to be under a Central Midwives Board consisting of five doctors and five other persons, one to be appointed by the Royal British Nurses Association. Qualification was one year in bona fide practice and a certificate of good character.

This had been backed by both the General Medical Council and the Royal College of Physicians—who were divided on the subject of registration of nurses as distinct from midwives.

Nevertheless the passing of the Act not only strengthened Ethel Bedford Fenwick in her own special campaign but the R.B.N.A. reversed its policy and came out directly for registration, drafting a Bill in the following year, which however was rejected by Parliament. Ethel Bedford Fenwick's Society for the State Registration of Nurses was also unsuccessful with a Bill of its own. The thing, however, was now becoming recognized as a public issue, the pros and cons being discussed in the general as well as all the medical and nursing Press apart from her own paper. As an outcome officialdom moved at last and a Select Committee was appointed to report on the matter in 1905.

Of all those who had prepared the ground upon which a national organization of trained nurses could be built Ethel Bedford Fenwick had done most. Yet although she had been so

cavalierly treated by her own R.B.N.A., she resisted the College
of Nursing, when it was later established, with all her strength.
Her over-high standards and determination to lift nursing to the
level of the medical profession—however impracticable at that
time—can be understood in a great part by an outline of what
nursing then amounted to and what its growth roots had been.

Obviously, nursing is as ancient as womankind. Before
recorded history, the male did not always triumph unscathed
over his prey or his enemy. If he survived at all the female
would normally do her best to restore him to health if only to
preserve a source of supply for herself and her children.

It was not until the end of the nineteenth century, however,
that nursing as trained and skilled craftsmanship came into
being. Before then there were numbers of devoted people doing
the best they knew for the sick, which was not much by modern
standards. However nursing, such as it was, was one of the
works of mercy enjoined by the Christian Church in A.D. 60.
Some five hundred years later St. Benedict laid down rules for
the care of the sick which were followed by the Catholic and
Protestant nursing orders in Europe and by the Red Cross.
The most notable of the earlier records are those of the Hotel
Dieu in Paris where the Augustinian Sisterhood practised from
the twelfth century.

Taking the world at large the list of religious nursing
organizations even in the Middle Ages is formidable. One can
only mention those best known among English-speaking
peoples—the Military Orders of the Knights Hospitaller of St.
John of Jerusalem, and the Sisters of Charity, still one of the
largest nursing orders in existence today.

At Kaiserwerth in Germany a pastor, Theodor Fliedner and
his wife, in 1836, influenced the development of modern nursing
by founding the Deaconess Movement, deaconesses being
Protestant women who served their Church by tending the sick
and the poor. Florence Nightingale spent three months there
as part of her general survey of nursing practice, but was not
impressed by the discipline or the standards. Still, Kaiserwerth
was one of the first places in the world where some attempt at
organized nurse training was carried out.

Miss Nightingale was one of those rare human beings who

can combine almost fanatical devotion to a cause with cool observation and shrewd judgement. She stands to the history of efficient nursing as Ethel Bedford Fenwick stands to the groundwork on which the organization of nurses was founded, but beyond comparison she was the greater individual. She had the mind of a practical scientist as well as the drive of a reformer. Her career is so well known that no more than an outline is necessary here.

Born of wealthy and highly connected parents in 1820 she studied nursing practice, sanitation, statistics, and medicine—as far as a woman was then allowed to study medicine—and opened her first institution for the care of the sick in London when she was thirty-four. It was in that year that the Secretary of State for War asked her to go with the army to the Crimea and undertake the nursing of the wounded. She accepted, chose a staff of practical nurses and Catholic and Anglican sisters, and went out to make one of the best-deserved of all historical reputations. In brief, by her organization, discipline, and method she reduced a death-rate that had been counted normal at 44 per 100, to 22 per 1,000!

When she returned she used a fund which was raised in her honour to found a school of nursing at St. Thomas's Hospital, London, which opened with fifteen probationers on 15 June 1860. This later became the pattern for schools of nursing all over the world, but for many years various of the rules she laid down were violently resisted. Those rules were:

First, the head and controller of any school of nursing must be a qualified nurse and not a clergyman. Although the great religious bodies had until then sponsored most of the effective care of the sick, their attitude to scientific discovery was not as free from the theological prejudices of the time as she knew was vitally necessary. She had also seen that denominational differences could produce furious antagonism, and realized that nursing, if it was to become the practical profession she intended it to be, must be entirely free of control by any who were not medically trained. For the rest, her rules demanded a practical scheme of planned teaching, recruiting from the most effective sources, and properly equipped homes and recreational quarters for the probationers. Finally she demanded special extra training for those nurses who undertook visiting among the sick poor.

By the latter end of the nineteenth century these general principles Florence Nightingale laid down were adopted by the schools established by voluntary and tax-supported hospitals in most English-speaking countries. The pioneer district nursing she established—the prototype of public health nursing—began in 1854. Midwifery, however, for a variety of reasons remained separate and was organized and established with a register at an earlier date than general nursing.

Florence Nightingale's work therefore is the first great practical stride from superstition and prejudice to scientific principles which was made in the care of the sick since the Dark Ages. But at the time she set her hand to the task general conditions had daunted many who tried their best but lacked her clear reasoning and indomitable fighting spirit.

CHAPTER THREE

The Reformers

FLORENCE NIGHTINGALE, contrary to much uninformed belief, had nothing to do with the Red Cross—although there have been illustrations of tents and buildings in the Crimea bearing red cross emblems. An outline of that organization has a place here, however, because the two principal founders of the College of Nursing in 1916 were Miss (later Dame) Sarah Swift, the British Red Cross Society's Matron in Chief, and the Hon. Arthur Stanley, Chairman of the Joint War Committee of the British Red Cross Society and Order of St. John.

The Red Cross came into being as a direct result of the war between France and Austria in the late 1850s. There was no medical organization on either side other than the regimental surgeons. Thus it came about that after the battle of Solferino in 1859 conditions were, if anything, worse than they had been in the Crimea. The wounded were left where they lay. Since there was no organization, even for a supply of bandages, the great mass of them just had to die where they were, or recover, as fate decreed.

Next morning a young civilian named Henri Dunant rode up a hill to see the battlefield and was shocked by the appalling scene. He rode into the nearest village and called together the inhabitants to take water to the wounded, to dress and bandage as far as they could, and to bring into shelter as many as could be loaded on to their carts.

When only the dead remained to be buried Dunant sought out the high officers of both sides. He convinced them that a medical organization was as necessary to an army as its weapons, for one reason which he knew would appeal to them above any other—which was that by his own work he had saved the lives of trained soldiers who could be used to fight again.

By that time Florence Nightingale's achievement was known

throughout the world, so that Dunant could remind the Continental generals of her success. Dunant thereafter wrote a vivid pamphlet 'Un Souvenir de Solferino' in which he described the appalling circumstances in which the bravest men of their countries were left to die. The pamphlet immediately caught public interest. It was translated into a number of languages. Finally Dunant found himself a member of a conference representing sixteen countries which assembled in Geneva. This eventually became the International Committee of the Red Cross—the symbol chosen being a red cross on a white background, the Swiss flag in reverse.

Each nation agreed to form its own Red Cross society, all being affiliated to the Central Committee in Geneva, numbering twenty-five Swiss citizens whose object was 'to create international agencies in war time for the relief of victims of war, especially prisoners of war, and to maintain fundamental Red Cross principles'. All nations who have signed the Geneva Convention co-operate to these ends.

Finally—although this is only the briefest outline of its gigantic work—the Red Cross has carried out Henri Dunant's suggestion in his pamphlet 'Un Souvenir de Solferino' that it should in peace time 'include the improvement of health, the prevention of disease, and the mitigation of suffering throughout the world'. As a result almost every British municipality has a branch of the Red Cross working in its area, visiting disabled Service personnel and crippled children, escorting patients to and from hospitals, and undertaking auxiliary nursing duties.

Another significant event in the history of nursing also took place in England, at much the same period as that of Henri Dunant's work.

William Rathbone, a wealthy native of Liverpool, started the first embryonic District Nursing Service by providing a nurse and the necessary medicaments for the nursing of poor people in their own homes for a period of three months in part of the city. This was a success and he decided to extend the service but could not obtain trained nurses. He applied to Florence Nightingale who suggested that nurses should be trained, along her lines, locally. Rathbone had a training school built together with a nurses' home and presented it to the Liverpool Royal Infirmary.

Three years later the scheme was so successful that the city had been divided into eighteen districts each under the charge of one of Rathbone's trained nurses. The necessary medicaments and food for the poor patients were provided by groups of ladies in each district.

As has always been the case, however, there were many people who could not be properly nursed or treated at home. At that time their only alternative was admission to the Parish Infirmary at Brownlow Hill. The nurses reported to Rathbone that most of the sufferers resisted the move frantically and said they preferred immediate death in their own beds. So he went to Brownlow Hill to find out why.

The place housed over a thousand helpless, aged, mostly incurable people in every stage of infectious and contagious disease. There were no trained nurses at all. What care the inmates got was from those of their number still able to move about, and from pauper women from the local workhouse. Many of these were alcoholics, or prostitutes down on their luck.

What food there was was badly cooked and only got to the helpless patients after the more active had taken the lion's share. Some of the wards containing mental cases were patrolled by policemen to 'keep order'. This was in 1866, and although Rathbone was almost as shocked as Dunant had been at Solferino, the infirmary was in reality neither worse nor better than the average throughout Britain at the period.

Rathbone decided that such conditions must not be allowed in a society that called itself civilized. He persuaded Florence Nightingale to send him a trained and experienced nurse from her school at St. Thomas's Hospital to act as Lady Superintendent of a new staff at Brownlow Hill. This was Agnes Jones whose name has a special lustre in nursing history. Her first report on Brownlow Hill was that it was 'Dante's Inferno' but she faced it without flinching. The first thing was to scrub and clean, and all patients fit for the work were set to it. Surprisingly a large number recovered of their ills very quickly and discharged themselves. Then Miss Jones, with Rathbone's enthusiastic backing, demanded reasonably decent bedding, sheets, washing facilities, and, of course, medicaments which were grudgingly supplied by the Vestry authorities.

She strove hard for a year to train the workhouse women to be something like nurses, and had them paid wages. But in this she failed. They were all too far gone in mental and moral degeneration to learn anything, and could not be trusted to carry out the easiest tasks without supervision. They usually drank their wages away on pay-night and were consequently useless next day. Agnes Jones gave up the attempt, and in the second year got a full staff of trained nurses (according to the standard of the time) with vastly different results. The Local Authority then began to realise that it was cheaper to pay fair wages to skilled women who could get patients well enough to leave, than to pay pauper-rates to those who kept the beds occupied. Agnes Jones's achievements had an historic result. The Local Authority took over full responsibility for her new standard of cleanliness and skilled attention to patients, and made the infirmary chargeable on the general rates.

But the strain of overwork on Miss Jones had a tragic result. In 1868, her third year of unremitting struggle, she became badly run-down but refused to take any rest. She caught typhus fever and as a result of her lack of resistance died after only a short illness. Florence Nightingale, deeply saddened, afterwards wrote of Agnes Jones: '. . . a woman attractive, rich, young, and witty . . . died as she had lived, at her post, in one of the largest workhouse infirmaries in the kingdom . . . In less than three years she had reduced one of the most disorderly hospital populations in the world to something like Christian discipline, and had converted a Vestry to the conviction of the economy, as well as the humanity, of nursing pauper sick by trained nurses.'

Agnes Jones, who could have lived to old age in luxury and comfort, gave her life as heroically as any fighting man in war. In doing so she not only paved the way for sweeping poor-law reforms but also had an effect on properly organized district nursing. Before going to Liverpool she had been keenly interested in the subject and had outlined to a Mrs. Ranyard a scheme for trained nurses to attend the poor in their own homes. After her death Mrs. Ranyard put her suggestions to practical effect, and organized a system whereby fully trained nurses should have special extra training for the work.

Meanwhile the district nursing begun by Rathbone (who became a Member of Parliament) spread from Liverpool to London, the first organization being started by the Hon. Mrs. Stuart Wortley and Robert Wigram in 1868. This was the East London Nursing Society which by its object to 'provide trained nursing for the sick poor in their own homes, without distinction of creed or nationality' proved an outstanding success, growing and expanding throughout all the eastern parishes. This is still continuing its fine work and now includes a number of male nurses. Next came the Metropolitan and National Nursing Association which Mr. Rathbone, M.P., also helped to found. A Central Home and Training School for nurses in district work was established in 1875, the first Lady Superintendent being a Nightingale nurse named Florence Lees who instituted a system that succeeded from the start. Like Ethel Bedford Fenwick in later years, Florence Lees believed that her nurses should always be recruited from among gentlewomen. Probably because Miss Lees's field was much smaller than the general world of hospital nursing envisaged by Ethel Bedford Fenwick —and received less publicity—her ideas were accepted, whereas those of the latter never proved practical. Florence Lees's gentlewomen served an initial month in the Central Home, then trained in a hospital for a year, and finally returned for another six months in the Central Home for specialized training.

The specialized training was necessary, indeed. So was the dedicated courage of those women who had come from well-off, smoothly managed homes.

Such women were not only in the vanguard of the emancipation of their sex which was the great movement of the period from the 'sixties onward. They were intelligent, well educated, courageous . . . and could find nothing to do worth the doing in the normal range of their lives. In some cases where a husband had died young, the normal occupation of home and bringing up children was not always enough for such minds.

There was, of course, the cruel and senseless so-called joke that those who lacked beauty must also lack men, and therefore gave themselves to good works. Florence Lees's attitude was that only gentlewomen brought up to a sense of honour could be trusted to work unsupervised in impoverished homes. This attitude was wrong, as Florence Nightingale knew well, and as time has shown, but owing to the fact that her period produced women who would face anything in order to feel that they had a useful place in life, her scheme was a success.

The preliminary field-work before the founding of the Metropolitan and National Nursing Association was the most important ever carried out in district nursing. Upon it the future organization throughout the country was founded. Before Miss Lees started work it was found that there were less than thirty trained nurses doing district visiting in the whole of London apart from the East End. The hospitals insisted that they could not afford to train women for poor-law work, and there were practically no sources of medical supplies available. Control, such as there was, had been in the hands of well-meaning, rather muddle-headed and not over-energetic people. This, of course, did not apply to the Eastern section of the great town where Mrs. Stuart Wortley's Nursing Society was already making history.

Under Florence Lees the 'Metropolitan' expanded and opened branches all over London. The system was taken up throughout the provinces and was established in Scotland and Ireland. The women of Britain contributed over £70,000 at the time of Queen Victoria's Jubilee in 1887 to a 'Women's Jubilee Fund', and the whole of this sum the Queen directed to be devoted to the furtherance of district nursing. Thus the 'Queen's Institute of District Nursing' came into being, affiliated to the 'Metropolitan Society'.

The history of district nursing moved faster than that of the long-overdue reform of the poor-law institutions. Agnes Jones's magnificent lead in Liverpool was followed quickly by London, but thereafter a decade passed before her system began to spread gradually across the country. In London, during Miss Jones's second year of work, Florence Nightingale enthusiastically backed a demand drawn up by H. B. Farnall, a

Poor Law inspector, that henceforth in infirmaries various categories of patients should be separated and given suitable treatment; these categories were the sick (in general), the insane, the incurable, and children.

This was made law by the Metropolitan Poor Act of 1867 from which dates the first real reform and civilized administration of infirmaries since the Dark Ages. Even so thirty years were to pass before pauper nurses were by law replaced by trained, paid nurses. During that period, however, there was a widespread 'clean up' of infirmaries on the Liverpool system, and medical and general administration and service vastly improved. New infirmaries were built as hospitals and run as hospitals with matrons, trained staff, and visiting doctors. As from 1878 the new reforms of the system spread across the land.

All were under the Local Government Board which, just after the First World War, was absorbed into the Ministry of Health. Ten years later in 1929 the Local Government Act transferred the responsibilities of all Boards of Guardians to County and Borough Councils who at the same time took over all poor-law infirmaries. In 1930 the official process began of turning the infirmaries into general hospitals. Under this measure the aged and incurable patients were transferred to other institutions, and the newly constituted hospitals were reorganized and equipped for medical and surgical general hospital work.

It is interesting to look back at the position at that time. All hospitals other than these reorganized infirmaries were supported by voluntary contributions, and most of them were already in very serious financial difficulties. The reorganized municipal hospitals had no financial worries at all; they were supported out of the ratepayers' money. They were staffed by able doctors, experienced matrons, and trained nurses, who were more highly paid than their sisters in the voluntary system.

One may wonder, after nearly forty years, why it was that those municipal hospitals, in such a comparatively favoured position, did not become the leading hospitals of the country. It is possible that they were prevented by the dead hand of 'Bumbledom,' the rigid, cautious system by which 'established' officials of any strata of government fear having to accept responsibility for any act of enterprise not covered by existing, printed rules. To be fair, it must be remembered that they were very new and their administrators naturally unsure of themselves.

Perhaps the answer lies somewhere between the two, but the fact remains that they had a magnificent chance which passed them by.

CHAPTER FOUR

First trained Nurses

BEFORE 1840 there were virtually no trained nurses—in the sense we regard training today—even in the great London hospitals. The women recruited for the work were described as 'capable' women, of the servant class and were generally unable to read or write. As a result they could learn little or nothing from doctors except to obey orders. There were among them, as there always will be, a certain number of 'born nurses', cheerful, energetic, and with a dedicated interest in healing—one meets more than one in the pages of Jane Austen. For the most part, however, they were careless, personally dirty, and incapable of doing anything much more than the work of charwomen. Florence Nightingale has left it on record that nursing at that period was done by those who were 'too old, too weak, too drunken, too stolid, or too bad to do anything else', all of which raises the vision of Charles Dickens's magnificent creation, Sairey Gamp—a piece of inspired clowning but an accurate enough portrait of the average. Sisters usually were recruited from a slightly better-educated class. There was a general rule that all convalescent patients had to help in the work of the nursing staff. In most poor-law institutions the only so-called nursing available was carried out by whatever paupers were capable of movement.

The pay of those who were called nurses varied very widely and is an indication of conditions even when an allowance is made for the difference in money values. The nursing staff at St. Thomas's at that period received 9s. 7d. per week plus an allowance of beer.

Those at St. George's got £16 per year plus 1s. a day board wages, a daily two pints of beer, and a weekly allowance of six pounds of bread.

At St. Bartholomew's the women fared more excitingly,

since they were allowed the meat from the hospital broth to go
with their daily half-loaf and pint of beer, and there was also
'dinner' on Sundays. They were allowed two gowns and one
cap per year. Sisters at Guy's, St. Thomas's, St. Mary's, and
St. George's were paid an annual £50, £37, £20, and £20
respectively and in addition were allowed the same bread and
beer rations as the nurses.

Although drunkenness was normal among nurses—indeed
among all the working people of the time—the beer-ration
referred to above had little significance in this respect. Most
of the larger hospitals brewed their own beer on their premises
just as they usually had their own bakeries. And indeed 'small'
beer was standard at the boys' meals in most public schools.

At this time and for many years afterwards hospitals were
feared by the general public and were only used by those who
could not afford nursing at home. This was natural since men
like Lister and Pasteur had not yet convinced the medical
profession of the existence of bacteria. There were no antiseptic
rules and regulations. Surgical instruments might be washed
clean of the last patient's blood but they were never even
boiled. Doctors operated in old frock-coats, heavy with dried
blood, and only washed their hands after their tasks were done.
Many of the great London hospitals were rat-ridden and
although attempts were made to rid incoming patients of
vermin they were far from satisfactory.

The resulting death-rate made normal people regard going
into hospital as the final step to the grave. The work-house
infirmaries held even greater terrors. They were largely used
as convenient places in which the hospitals could get rid of
patients they were unable to cure. But since local authorities
did not want to encourage paupers to 'loaf in bed', the standard
of food and the general conditions were allowed to become so
revolting that only those stayed who were finally resigned to
death.

Better-off people in cases of serious sickness employed nurses
in their homes—nurses recommended by their doctors or
supplied by hospitals and agencies. These women made what
was then regarded as a good living—from £1. 1s. to £1. 10s. a
week including board, lodging, and washing. They varied

enormously in type and ability. As certain societies and religious bodies tried to institute some form of training during the next twenty years, doctors found that they could call upon some really useful and reliable women.

There were, however, still the illiterate nurses from hospitals and agencies who were no more use than charwomen. There were nurses who were pleased to offer themselves in prostitution to the males of a household. There were nurses who were accomplished thieves—and who were from time to time caught and imprisoned but thereafter went back to 'private practice' as blithely as ever.

Florence Nightingale was, above all, clear headed. These were the conditions she saw around her in her youth, but she realized that they were so much an ingrained part of nursing, almost hallowed by centuries of custom, that they could not be swept away by any sudden measure of reform. She knew the process must be gradual because those in charge of the administration and finance must first be cajoled into altering time-honoured rules. This could only be done if she could prove that the necessary changes would 'pay' better—that properly trained nurses and clean and sanitary hospitals would result in less bed-ridden pauperism, and less danger of epidemics which struck down rich and poor alike. To the end of her life she was against any form of state registration because she was certain that the only worth-while recommendation of a nurse would be from the sister, matron, or doctor who had actual experience of her work and character.

Meanwhile, there is no doubt that Ethel Bedford Fenwick did not realize the full effect of the new mass-education. This certainly failed to teach the mass average even to read, write, or figure—in which it still fails even today with an appreciable percentage. What it did, however, was to make education in stages available free to those whose minds were capable of assimilating it. The younger women of the period who genuinely wanted to become nurses were just the type to whom free education was most useful. They knew of the growing movement for the emancipation of their sex. They saw that in gaining knowledge lay their greatest strength. The result was that the best minds of any class, to the lowest, reached eagerly for the new gift, and so in a few years a new strata of woman-kind emerged in Britain.

They were of no single class. They spoke with any and every accent and dialect according to their background. But having learned to read they found their minds hungry for stronger nourishment than the thin love-stories of the time. They became suffragettes, either active or passive. Those who became nurses were also glad to read and study the technical material made available.

It was obviously beyond the comprehension of Ethel Bedford Fenwick that some nurses who spoke the argot of her servants were in many cases better educated by their own, post-school efforts than a number of her lady probationers, and were also by reason of their strength of character every bit as reliable. This was because in the classes whose daughters ranked as ladies most fathers thought educating girls a waste of money, and most mothers were terrified of girls turning out 'clever' and thus frightening off eligible young men. If a girl could read an invitation and write a formal bread-and-butter letter it was enough.

The beginnings of reform in the general condition of nursing began in about 1840. Louisa Twining, daughter of a wealthy tea merchant, set herself the task of visiting all the workhouses and infirmaries in the London area, and publicizing the appalling conditions therein. The famous Elizabeth Fry, who had been to Kaiserwerth long before Florence Nightingale, founded in 1840 the English Protestant Sisters of Charity. Five years later came the nursing order founded by the High Church movement, led by Pusey. Priscilla Sellon initiated the Sisters of Mercy in 1848.

These were the best known of a great number of women who were courageous enough to attack the problem and try to awaken the conscience of the general public. They prepared the way for the great reforms set in motion by Florence Night-ingale in 1860. In justice to Ethel Bedford Fenwick it must be admitted that from 1867 the Nightingale School allowed lady pupils to pay for maintenance during training, although it was laid down firmly that 'we only want gentlewomen who come with settled purpose to do the work, free from all romance and affectation'. Still, this after all, was more practical than the Bedford Fenwick assumption that the training of ladies only, would ensure fewer failures.

The Nightingale School at St. Thomas's Hospital had trained nearly 2,000 nurses by the year 1903. The standard of training and the type of recruits chosen resulted in a general quality of nurses far above all previous average. The school became known, justifiably, as a training ground for matrons, since Florence Nightingale had every good reason for seeing that her star pupils were recommended to the best appointments in the country.

By 1887 women from her school were matrons or superintendents at Westminster, Paddington, Marylebone, Highgate, Edinburgh, Huntingdon, Leeds, Lincoln, Liverpool, Southampton, and Salisbury. All of them were, of course, her disciples who strove to establish their own training schools on her model. Meanwhile scores of the nurses she had trained were rising in the hierarchy of all the great London teaching hospitals, and others were members of the various nursing organizations that had come into being—Queen Alexandra's Imperial Military Nursing Service, formed just after the Boer War, the Royal Naval Nursing Service (1902), and the Territorial Army Nursing Service (1907). By 1914, in addition to Ethel Bedford Fenwick's Royal British Nurses Association, her Society for the State Registration of Nurses, and her Matrons' Council, there were a number of other nursing organizations and societies, but not one had gained a commanding position. At the outbreak of war a large number of young women joined the Voluntary Aid Detachments which had been organized in 1909 by a joint committee of the British Red Cross Society and the Order of St. John of Jerusalem. Most of the girls were given instruction in first aid but practically none had received nursing training. They wore a spectacular uniform with large red crosses on the cap and bosom. Many of them gained the ardently desired jobs of nursing handsome young wounded officers in converted mansion hospitals.

Taking the whole picture of the war, the mass of the V.A.D.s did a good and courageous job. The available force of trained nurses was spread thin, so something had to be done about the

3

effective training of the more intelligent of the V.A.D.s—
and for that matter about recruitment in general to the profession. It was, however, a profession without any really
representative organization, effective in nature, even including
Ethel Bedford Fenwick's R.B.N.A., which had failed to
attract a membership of significant numbers.

At this point another woman of vivid personality and driving
strength of character decided that nursing must have a
dominant organization to which all members of the profession
could turn for leadership, representation, and help. She was
Miss (later Dame) Sarah Swift, one of the most famous matrons
of Guy's Hospital, a clever if imperious woman . . . who stood
slightly less than five feet in height.

CHAPTER FIVE

The College Founders

SARAH SWIFT was born in 1854 at Kirton, Boston, Lincs, daughter of a prosperous landowner. She had, in her own phrase, an 'instinct' for nursing, and although possessed of comfortable means enrolled as a probationer at Dundee Infirmary in 1877. Directly she had finished training she was appointed Acting Matron of Dundee Home for Incurables and was subsequently Matron of the City Infirmary, Liverpool, and the London Fever Hospital.

Sarah Swift loved travelling and could afford it. In 1889 she went to New York to see conditions of nursing in America, and within a year of further wanderings found herself appointed Superintendent of the Nursing Section of the Seamen's Hospital at—of all places—Constantinople.

However, she eventually returned to England and in 1898 entered Guy's Hospital. Two years later, in 1900, she was appointed Matron.

It was typical of Sarah Swift's abounding energy that after retiring from Guy's Hospital, in 1909, she still carried out some of the most important work of her life. Soon after the outbreak of the First World War in 1914 the Nurses Department of the British Red Cross Society was formed. This Sarah Swift took over and ran with outstanding success until the war was finished. She was decorated with the Royal Red Cross, the O.B.E., the title of Lady of Grace of St. John of Jerusalem, and finally created Dame Grand Cross of the British Empire.

Although minute in stature she had immense force of personality, rigid dignity—and a sharp humour which could sometimes be terrifying to juniors.

While Matron of Guy's it was her habit to make unheralded surprise visits to the wards at any hour. Naturally, the nursing staff did their best to arrange a look-out system to pass warning

of her approach, and on one occasion a young probationer
having received the warning, got on to the speaking-tube to the
next ward. Having heard her call answered, she said, quietly,
'Look out! The old girl's on her way.' At which same moment
Sarah Swift's voice, close behind her, murmured, 'Look out!
The old girl's here!'

All matrons of that period were what would be called fiercely
autocratic in these days. Sarah Swift was perhaps a more rigid
disciplinarian than the average, yet she was genuinely liked as
well as respected by those who worked with her and for her.
Autocracy in her case did not mean that only she must be in
the forefront, and that only her special ideas were sacrosanct.
Her mind was flexible and she could 'get on' with people of
power not actually in the profession. Her imaginative and
enterprising qualities are shown in the fact that during her life
she found time to help establish a trained nursing service in
H.M. Prisons.

This grey-eyed, determined little woman, known (behind her
back) by all her staff as 'the mighty atom' sought out one of the
ablest administrators of the time, the Hon. (later Sir) Arthur
Stanley, Chairman of the British Section of the Red Cross
and Treasurer of St. Thomas's Hospital. Folding a hand over
each elbow in an habitual pose—and sitting in a chair with her
small feet clear of the floor—Sarah Swift said typically:

'Well, Mr. Stanley, you see it's like this. Nursing is in a state
of chaos, no one knows where to turn for authority and
direction. So I have come to you to suggest the formation of an
effective central body—a College of Nursing—in some smaller
way analogous to the Colleges of Physicians and Surgeons.
Will you help us?'

Mr. Stanley said 'Yes'. He had twinkling blue-grey eyes, a
very considerable knowledge of people in general—and of
Sarah Swift in particular. If she was prepared to give her
excellent mind and abounding energy to a project, he was
willing to back it as a general principle. During the next half-
hour they discussed the outline, each suggesting names for the
proposed council of the college and drawing up a list.

Arthur Stanley was a typical member of the Derby family,
burly, urbane, something of a dandy in dress—but, tragically,

physically crippled so that he could only get about leaning heavily on sticks and supported by his faithful man, Charles. But he knew more about the world of hospital work, to which he had devoted his life, and the people in it than almost any other man.

'You know there will be antagonism to this?' he asked with a smile.

'Yes, and I know from whom it will come,' said Sarah Swift. There was no need for either of them to mention Ethel Bedford Fenwick who already regarded herself as the leader of the nursing profession, although her ideas were well known to be in many ways contrary to those of the still living Florence Nightingale.

Sarah Swift had ideas that ran contrary to the tenets of both those dominating figures. She wanted registration of bona fide nurses of good character irrespective of class. She wanted a standardized system of training laid down and a written examination to follow, in which educational standards were to be subordinate to technical knowledge.

'You will need money,' said Arthur Stanley cheerfully, 'and a headquarters office, anyway, in which to start. Well, I'll talk to Cooper Perry and we will write around to the training schools and doctors, first. Money ain't easy to get, of course, but it'll come in if we get the right people on our side.'

The 'ain't' was one of his pet, harmless poses. It had been a Victorian fashion to drop an 'h' here and there and use an odd cockneyism.

Sarah Swift was perfectly satisfied with the interview—as, knowing him, she had expected to be. Between them in the next few weeks they contacted the four other people who were to be responsible for the real founding of the College.

First was Mr. (later Sir) Cooper Perry, Medical Superintendent of Guy's Hospital.

Cooper Perry's career had been a matter of astonishment to many who knew him. He had been Head of the School at Eton and collected classical prizes with apparent facility and ease. At Cambridge he repeated his 'habit of success' in the Classical Tripos and was made a Fellow of King's. Since it was generally accepted that he intended entering the Church it was murmured confidentially among his seniors that here was an Archbishop of Canterbury in the making.

The Church had, indeed, been his first intended career, but when he faced the fact of ordination certain matters of faith—which he never discussed with others—troubled his conscience. He therefore turned to the only other career in which he felt his life could be devoted to the good of his fellow men, which was the study of medicine. Although one who throughout life had a quick wit and a great sense of fun, he was inwardly devout and unswerving in what he felt to be his duty.

A brilliant, successful, and indeed well-known scholar with a ready-made and easy career in School or Church ahead of him, Cooper Perry renounced it all and entered himself humbly as an ordinary student at the London Hospital. Since he had the habit of learning and concentration, and a brilliant intellect as well, he qualified with as apparent ease as he had picked up his prizes at Eton. As the years passed he accumulated an immense knowledge of Morbid Anatomy and of diseases of the skin.

It was at Guy's Hospital, however, that he found the outlet for his amazing powers of organization and administration.

In 1888 he became Dean of the Medical School. In 1893 he accepted the position of Superintendent of the Hospital and for over thirty years devoted his life to the complete reorganizing and modernizing of the general system. Only once or twice was he to be persuaded to give his mind to other matters. At the recommendation of the Royal College of Physicians he went to Cairo to reorganize the Faculty of Medicine in the Egyptian University, and at home he became Chairman of the Distributing Committee of the King Edward's Hospital Fund for London.

He, above all men, knew the confused warring of elements among the various nursing associations, and the immense work done by the autocratic Mrs. Bedford Fenwick. In his own life's work he was no autocrat although he had the power to be so. His first rule was to make himself accessible to all at Guy's who came with plaints or suggestions, and the latter he would always consider with an open mind—backed by great experience and shrewdness. The tiny but dynamic Sarah Swift he had also known for years and deeply respected as one who could carry others with her by convincing argument, as well as she could hold high command.

In size and stature he was her very opposite. A bulky, heavy man, lumbering in walk and awkward in movement, he yet had sensitive, highly mobile hands famous among his surgical students. In his office or on the wards he was a happy man, warmly benign to patients and paternal with students and nurses. But outside these activities, at any form of party (if he could be dragged there at all) he was miserably, painfully shy.

This, however, never affected his work with young people of whom he had instinctive understanding. As a result—although in this the account runs somewhat too far ahead—he became a great success as Principal Officer of London University, an appointment he accepted after his retirement from Guy's in 1920.

Among those he and Sarah Swift decided to invite to a 'founders' discussion' to launch the suggested College of Nursing was a woman for whom both had liking and genuine respect.

Rachael Annie Cox-Davies, Matron of the Royal Free Hospital, entered the scheme with her typical energy and enterprise. She it was who was to gain the allegiance of the first Viscountess Cowdray, who later gave the College its present buildings, at a cost in the region of half a million pounds.

No two women more physically dissimilar than Rachael Cox-Davies and Sarah Swift could well have been found, although both possessed forceful personality, energy, determination, and self confidence. Rachael Cox-Davies was as tall as Sarah Swift was short, with a full figure that gave her an imposing—to juniors a formidable—presence. Neither had the slightest hesitation in laying down the law or maintaining what today would be thought a harsh and inflexible discipline. Yet where Sarah Swift would reach her decisions by a quick and skilful weighing of facts, Rachael Cox-Davies seemed to have that sixth sense of 'feeling' the solution of any problem, which is popularly attributed to those of Welsh ancestry. Be that as it may—she was almost inevitably right.

Where facts merited it both could be compassionate and

kind, but equally in some cases intolerant, inconsequent—and frankly pig-headed. It has happened before in a variety of activities that some one period produced dominant and outstanding characters. In nursing the period from 1860 to 1914 produced a number of women like Sarah Swift and Rachael Cox-Davies—veritable giants of personality and achievement. Such individuals are never easy to deal with, largely because the only argument which can really mean anything to them is that of a power greater than their own. Yet it is people of this dominating, overbearing nature who are necessary to the founding of almost any new enterprise—and who have appeared so often just when they were needed.

Rachael Cox-Davies trained at Newport County Infirmary in 1889, and went to St. Bartholomew's in 1893 where she was successively ward sister, night sister, acting home sister, and office assistant until 1899 when she went to the South African War with the Army Nursing Service.

After her return at the end of the war she was appointed Matron of the Devon and Exeter Hospital in 1903. Later she became Matron of the New Hospital for Women in Soho Square, London, and in 1905 was appointed Matron of the Royal Free Hospital, holding the position for the next seventeen years, until she retired from nursing in 1922. From 1914 to the end of the war she was also Matron of the 1st London General Hospital for service cases, a temporary hospital of about 1,000 beds.

Rachael Cox-Davies was one of the best and most fluent public speakers the nursing profession has ever known. With Alicia Lloyd Still she was instrumental in launching the Association of Hospital Matrons* in 1919. Quite apart from her work in co-founding the College of Nursing she was also one of the co-founders of the Cowdray Club, of which details will be given as it has its place in the story. Incidentally she was an elected member of the Council of the College (later the Royal College) of Nursing from its inception to the day of her death in 1944.

Third of the four women most concerned in founding the

* As distinct from the Matrons' Council formed by Ethel Bedford Fenwick in 1894.

Left: Dame Sarah Swift

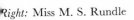

Right: Miss M. S. Rundle

Mrs Bedford Fenwick

Lady Cowdray

An early nineteenth century hospital scene depicted by Rowlandson

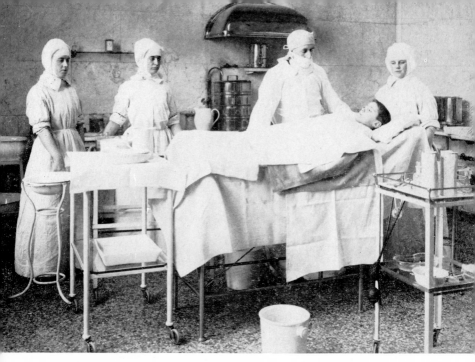

Above: The Hospital for Sick Children. One of the operating theatres
at the latter part of the nineteenth century

Below: One of ten operating theatres at Guy's Hospital, London, 1962

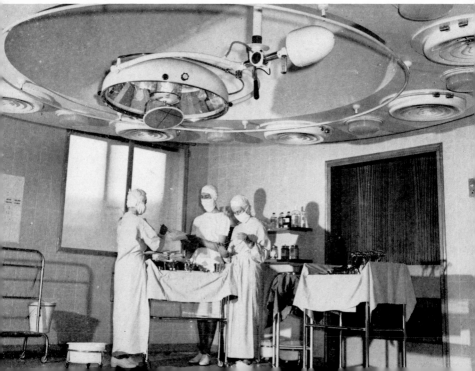

College was Alicia Lloyd Still, in 1916 Matron of St. Thomas's Hospital, who had been one of Florence Nightingale's personally chosen trainees at the Nightingale Training School at that hospital from 1897 to 1899. Afterwards she became Sister Charity and Sister of St. Thomas's Home.

A woman of outstanding ability, she soon made her way into the upper reaches of the profession. She was appointed Matron of Brompton Hospital in 1904, Matron of the Middlesex Hospital in 1909, and Matron of her own old Training School in 1913, a position she held for nearly twenty-five years. During the First World War she was placed in charge of both the civil and military work at St. Thomas's as Matron of the 5th London General Hospital from 1914 to the Armistice.

From the first she was enthusiastic for the College of Nursing, but both before and after the College was launched she was untiring in any labours that offered a benefit to nursing. In later years she became President of the Association of Hospital Matrons, a member of the General Nursing Council, a member of Queen Alexandra's Imperial Nursing Board and the Army Nursing Committee.

She became President of the Florence Nightingale International Foundation and President of the International Council of Nurses. Her decorations were R.R.C. (1917), C.B.E. (1917), and D.B.E. (1934); Florence Nightingale Medal (1933), and Medaille d'Honneur de l'Assistance Publique, and Lady of Grace of the Order of St. John of Jerusalem (1921).

Of these two latter women founders of the College their juniors have said that, apart from inspiring genuine respect and not a little fear, they were both at times so generally tiresome as almost—but never quite—to produce exasperated rebellion. All of which is a very normal characteristic of their type.

Alicia Lloyd Still, as a Nightingale protégée, was above all things practical, and believed in rigid military discipline. The correct wearing of uniform and regulation dressing of the nurses' hair were with her almost evangelical beliefs. Delinquents in these respects were subject to thunderbolts of humiliation that even some of her senior staff regarded as absurdities.

All this was in spite of the fact that however rigidly she

dressed her own tight *coiffure*, there were always rebellious wisps of hair that escaped to bob treacherously over the back of her starched collar . . . to the silent delight of all her juniors.

As a highly perceptive woman she was quite conscious that by the massive dignity of her own deportment she could strike terror into all and sundry. Yet there were many who could bear witness to the fact that she was genuinely feminine and quite capable of feeling and showing warm compassion where it was merited.

Alicia Lloyd Still had, further, the distinction of inventing the office of 'Sister Tutor'. This was in 1913 when, having reorganized the Training School at St. Thomas's and produced a new curriculum for a three-year course, she placed a sister in charge of all instruction. Incidentally it was this curriculum which was the basis upon which the first examination syllabus was compiled by the General Nursing Council. The first Sister Tutor to be appointed was Marion Agnes Gullen who had been at Middlesex Hospital with Alicia Lloyd Still.

One of the greatest living gynaecologists and most outstanding medical personalities of his time, Mr. (later Sir) Comyns Berkeley, M.C., M.D. (Cantab.), F.R.C.P., F.R.C.S., F.R.C.O.G., M.M.S.A. (Hon.), gave his active help and enthusiastic support to the founding of the College. A member of the first Council, he was appointed the first Honorary Treasurer, an office he continued to hold until his death in 1946.

Born in 1865, he was educated at Marlborough and Caius, Cambridge, and entered Middlesex Hospital as a student in 1888. A brilliant scholar, he later became Consulting Obstetric and Gynaecological Surgeon at Middlesex Hospital; Consulting Obstetrical Surgeon, City of London Lying In Hospital; Consulting Surgeon, Chelsea Hospital for Women; Examiner in Midwifery and Diseases of Women to Oxford and Cambridge and most of the Universities of the United Kingdom, and Chairman of the Central Midwives Board.

In addition to his outstanding medical instinct and skill was an ability to write clearly and illuminatingly. Writing was to him a pleasure, but he gave his talent practically exclusively to his absorbing interests, gynaecology and obstetrics. As is apparent from his books, he was wholeheartedly interested in helping to ensure that nurses and midwives got the best training possible in his specialized field.

CHAPTER SIX

The College of Nursing Ltd.

THE ARTICLES OF ASSOCIATION were skilfully drawn up by
Cooper Perry, and the College of Nursing was registered as
a limited company on 27 March 1916.
The principal objects of the College were:

(1) to promote the better education and training of nurses
and the advancement of nursing as a profession in all or any
of its branches.
(2) to promote uniformity of curriculum.
(3) to recognise approved nursing schools.
(4) to make and maintain a register of persons to whom
certificates of proficiency or of training and proficiency had
been granted.
(5) to promote Bills in Parliament for any object connected
with the interests of the nursing profession and, in particular,
with nurse education, organization, protection, or for their
recognition by the state.

As a start, nurses applying for entry on the College Register
were required to have had training in civil hospitals or infirmaries with at least 250 beds and having a resident medical
or surgical officer. At least one course of lectures per year must
have been given, and a final examination held before certificates
were issued.
From the first, until the College had its own premises, the
Council meetings were held at the Royal Automobile Club in
Pall Mall, which became the original registered office. The
Hon. Arthur Stanley was elected Chairman, Cooper Perry,
Hon. Secretary, and Comyns Berkeley, Hon. Treasurer. A sub-
committee was appointed to meet representatives of various
societies for state registration, and training schools were invited

to send representatives to a meeting at St. Thomas's Hospital to discuss the formation of a Consultative Board.

At the fourth Council meeting Miss Mary Rundle was appointed Secretary, thereby starting a lifetime of selfless and dedicated work to the newly founded organization.

The Chairman meanwhile had written to nurse-training schools and societies of trained nurses setting forth what everyone knew well enough—the fact that although there were many organizations for nurses they had no central directing policy. Moreover, while State registration was highly desirable so that the public could know a trained from an untrained nurse, there were many reasons why it was feared. It was not even welcomed by Florence Nightingale.

The letter invited them to send representatives to a meeting to be held at St. Thomas's Hospital on 7 April to discuss the formation of the Consultative Board, which was to be set up under the Articles of Association to advise the Council on courses of study and technical training for persons intended for the nursing profession and the conditions under which recognition might be extended to nursing schools.

It was a very clever letter because it made a direct appeal to nurses by the assurance that the College should ultimately be controlled by nurses democratically elected. Moreover it came from a man who, although a layman, was well known as leader of the British Red Cross Society. He also had the tact to show that the College (anyway as yet) was not committed to the controversial subject of State registration—although both he and Sarah Swift privately had it clearly enough determined in their minds.

The essence of the letter lay in the paragraphs:

'I am convinced that something should be done at once to co-ordinate the various interests involved, and, without prejudice to ultimate developments . . . my own view is that . . . we must rely upon a voluntary scheme of co-operation among the nurse-training schools throughout the country . . .

'Just as the Royal College of Physicians and Surgeons through the conjoint Board organize the teaching and examination of medical students . . . so do I feel most strongly that now is the right time for some such movement in the nursing profession . . .

'The promoters (of the College) having obtained the sanction of the Board of Trade to the registration of the College . . . should appoint the first Council of Management, two-thirds of whom should be Matrons of hospitals or Superintendents of Nursing, or Sisters or Nurses still engaged in the active practice of their profession.' *

The result was triumphant and immediate. At the first Ordinary General Meeting of the College on 18 May 1916 the Chairman was able to announce that over seventy training schools and societies had nominated representatives to the Consultative Board.

It was also reported that a meeting had been arranged for the following day at the R.A.C. with representatives of the various Societies for the State Registration of Nurses to confer with the Legal Registration Committee of the College.

Even Ethel Bedford Fenwick had written as Hon. Nursing Secretary of the Central Committee for the State Registration of Nurses giving a list of delegates therefrom to be headed by herself.

With the adoption of the Report the first official year in the life of the College was completed. It had been well conceived and expertly formed by two of the most able and experienced administrators in the hospital world. Its aims were fair to all, completely practical, and formulated by a Council who wanted the most efficient nursing service that could be organized without distinction of class.

As a result it was a resounding success from the start. At the next Ordinary General Meeting in a year's time the Chairman was able to announce a nurse-membership of over 7,000.

Meanwhile as a result of a meeting in Edinburgh in May the Scottish Board of the College was formally established in September. Premises were taken at 122 George Street. Professor James Ritchie, M.D., F.R.C., was elected Chairman, Professor John Glaister, M.D., D.P.H., Vice-Chairman, and Miss A. W. Gill, R.R.C., Hon. Secretary and Treasurer. In

* See Appendix, p. 197.

January of the following year Miss Mary A. Brunton was appointed first Secretary to the Board.

In order to launch the Scottish Board the sum of £300 was voted by the Council of the College, a gesture made possible by the sweeping success which had immediately followed its founding.

In the early part of the following year, 1917, Rachael Cox-Davies and Mary Rundle went to Dublin and Belfast and arranged meetings with the executives of the leading hospitals, and so founded the Irish Board which came into being in February 1917 under the Chairmanship of George Peacocke, M.D., F.R.C.P.I. Later Miss Harriet E. Reed became Hon. Secretary and a reading and rest-room was opened for members at 23 Kildare Street, Dublin.

Mary Rundle soon proved herself a key figure in the development of the College. She was born at Saltash, Cornwall, in 1874, and had two brothers who shared her great energy and acumen, one becoming Medical Superintendent of the Fazackerley Hospital in Liverpool, and the other becoming an Engineer-Admiral in the Royal Navy.

Miss Rundle's career was based upon a tragedy. She became engaged to a naval officer who died before their wedding-day. She at once decided to devote her life to nursing and, against the strong opposition of her family, entered herself as a probationer at St. Bartholomew's Hospital. After taking the full training she won the first Isla Stewart Scholarship, and went to New York where she took a further advanced course in hospital economics and studied teaching methods and curricula in various American nurse-training schools. In the course of her work she also took her certificate in massage.

After her return to England Mary Rundle became Assistant Matron under Rachael Cox-Davies at the Royal Free Hospital, and in 1912 was appointed Matron of the Royal Hospital for Diseases of the Chest. To this position she added, in 1915, the Matronship of the London General Hospital, Territorial Army Nursing Service, and was later awarded the Royal Red Cross. Mary Rundle organized some of the earliest post-graduate courses for nurses on tuberculosis nursing and health visiting and started her own nursing library.

It had been by special permission of the Director General of Medical Services that she applied for the Secretaryship of the College of Nursing while it was still in the process of formation. She believed implicitly in the idea of it as expressed by Sarah Swift and elaborated by Arthur Stanley. From that date for the next seventeen and a half years until her retirement she lived only for the building of the College into the greatest of the nursing organizations. Her great knowledge of nursing affairs was invaluable in her position. Her capacity for work was formidable. But she was repaid by seeing, before her retirement, the College membership total within a few hundreds of 30,000 general trained nurses.

Mary Rundle started her secretaryship in a tiny room in Vere Street, but finished it in a well-appointed office in the fine building which was given by the late Lady Cowdray. By that time a Royal Charter had also been granted.

Some of Mary Rundle's most important work was in helping to initiate the Federated Superannuation Scheme for Nurses and Hospital Officers, and she represented the interests of nurses on its Council until her death in 1937. She was awarded the Diploma in Nursing (*honoris causa*) Leeds University in 1925 and during her life was a member of the Advisory Board of the Diploma in Nursing, University of London, Vice-President of Bart's Nurses League, and a member of the first Council of the Cowdray Club.

No outline of Mary Rundle's career would be complete without mention of great friend and colleague Gertrude Cowlin, who joined her as Assistant Secretary of the College in 1917, and whose application for membership was dated 3 August 1916. The two met when they were training at Bart's and Miss Cowlin also studied nursing in America. She later became Assistant Matron to Miss Rundle at 1st London General Hospital, Territorial Army Nursing Service, and for the rest of their careers the two worked together.

Each exactly balanced the other. Mary Rundle was deliberate in method, precise and careful in thought, unvarying in temperament, a first-class executive in making workable and practical any scheme or idea that was set before her. Gertrude

Cowlin, on the other hand, was volatile, bubbling with ideas, mercurial in temperament, and impatient of anything that smacked of obstruction or red tape. During her training she had constantly been in trouble with authority over the petty restrictions that plagued hospitals of the period. Throughout her life, indeed, she could never resist the aiming of a mental peashooter at any form of pomposity. Her absorbed interest in nursing technique and outstanding general ability, allied with good looks and an impulsively generous nature, however, ensured her popularity with seniors as well as juniors.

At the College of Nursing, Gertrude Cowlin was, in turn, Assistant Secretary, Registrar, Organizing Secretary of the Local Centres, Chief of the Information Bureau, and Librarian. Additionally in 1924 she was appointed Education Officer as well as Librarian. She also made a specialized study of private nursing conditions. Subsequently she was appointed Editor of *The Nursing Times*.

As first Librarian of the Library of Nursing, which was established as the result of a grant from the Carnegie United Kingdom Trust, Gertrude Cowlin might in fact be regarded as its founder, since she collected a nucleus of books about which her followers could build what is now one of the best Libraries of any professional body.

When the great work of the original founders was gathering momentum in 1916 a quiet young girl wearing a 'flapper's' plait and bow of the time applied for a temporary job in the Vere Street office, and was taken on to address envelopes and make herself generally useful. She deserves a special niche in this account for two reasons, the first being that from that day her 'temporary' service with the College extended, unbroken, for forty-five and a half years until her retirement in 1961. The second is that she made herself so useful that she received early promotion and eventually had charge of all members' records, thereby making herself one of the most knowledgeable—and reliable—members of the staff. This was Miss D. Thomas whose record exceeds only by a matter of months that of Miss E. L. Obey who joined her as assistant but moved to the Finance Department when it was established in 1922, of which she

4

became chief clerk in 1934, and retired after completing forty-five years' service in 1964.

These two ladies, Miss Obey and Miss Thomas, achieved a record of service which is unlikely to be equalled. They were enthusiastic about the objects of the College from the start and gave it a loyalty and conscientiousness of work of which only such sterling characters are capable.

*   *   *

The success of the College in attracting nurse-membership from all over what was then the British Empire was not matched in its struggle to get an agreement on terms for state registration.

At the Council meeting on 1 June 1916 the Chairman had to report that the meeting of the College Legal Registration Committee with Ethel Bedford Fenwick and the delegates of other societies had failed. No basis of agreement could be found and he feared that any further negotiations to try and produce an agreed Bill would be abortive. The Central Committee for the State Registration of Trained Nurses had prepared and presented a Bill to Parliament and would not agree to the amendment of certain clauses which the College Committee regarded as wrongly conceived. Mrs. Bedford Fenwick and her delegates had strong influence, and showed no willingness to consider give-and-take or compromise. Eventually, however, the Central Committee's Bill was rejected by Parliament.

CHAPTER SEVEN

Registration Preliminaries

THE CHAIRMAN said that in these circumstances he had drafted a Bill after careful consultation with the Hon. Sir Charles Russell and Mr. Vezey Knox, Parliamentary Counsel.

The general principles of this proposed Bill were:

(1) That the College of Nursing Ltd. shall keep the legal register under the Act.

(2) That the register already formed by the College shall be the first register under the Act.

(3) That the Council of the College shall be constituted by rules drafted by the Council and approved by the Privy Council, with the proviso that at least two-thirds of the members of the Council shall be elected by the vote of the nurses on the register.

He offered this for the approval of the Council and added that he was anxious that this clear statement of the College's intended position should be put to the next meeting of persons nominated for the Consultative Board by various training schools on 15th of the month. This was unanimously agreed.

At the same meeting the College Registration Committee reported on certain details in the current Bill presented to Parliament by the Central Committee for the State Registration of Trained Nurses. Ethel Bedford Fenwick had watered down many of her original demands in this but even her advisers had little hope of it becoming law.

The College Registration Committee, however, now announced that after careful consideration the conditions suggested for admission of nurses to the State Register in the Central Committee's Bill had their approval.

These were that trained nurses already in practice should be admitted to the Register during three years after the passing of any Registration Act provided that:

(1) Applicant must be at least twenty-one and of good character.

(2) She must hold a certificate of training from a hospital or hospitals approved by such Act or from institutions wholly or partly maintained out of rates and recommended by the Local Government Board concerned.

(3) Or she must hold a certificate of similar training as a nurse authorized by the Lords Commissioners of the Admiralty for the sick bay staff of the Royal Navy or as a nurse authorized by the Army Council.

(4) Or she must hold a certificate from the Local Government Board for Ireland (this of course was many years before the Republic), that she was qualified under section 58 of the Local Government (Ireland) Act 1898, or she must hold a certificate from the Local Government Board for Scotland as prescribed thereby.

(5) Or she must produce evidence satisfactory to the Council of training prescribed by the Council's rules and have in addition served as a nurse for at least three years in a naval or military hospital.

In general the regulations also allowed nurse training 'as prescribed by the rules' to be certificated not only by hospitals but by infirmaries and poor-law infirmaries but laid down a minimum period of three years in each case.

The College of Nursing 'found itself in full agreement' with the foregoing, but recommended additional regulations concerning nurses applying within three years from July 1916:

(1) The applicant not less than twenty-one to hold a certificate of three years' training in a nurse-training school or school recognized by the Council.

(2) Or to hold a certificate of not less than two years' training in such training school followed by at least two years' bona fide practice as a nurse.

(3) Or to produce evidence of having taken training at a date to the satisfaction of the Council followed by at least five years in practice as a nurse.

It will be apparent that Ethel Bedford Fenwick had come a long, long way from her original, imperious demands and had realized the solid common sense of Florence Nightingale's attitude. The country had to have nurses—more and more nurses every year—so that it would be impossible to deny further employment to women of decent character who had been practising for an appreciable time. Among them there were the good, the bad, and the very much worse. The College, in its Bill, naturally hoped to eliminate the last, but as a matter of practical politics the great mass of nurses already in the land were the only nucleus from which a sufficient force of good and well-trained women could be developed.

The problem of the V.A.D. position was automatically solved in the registration rules as drafted by the College. Once the war was over, genuine nurses of full training need no longer fear to find themselves supplanted in the best positions by women who had not troubled to train seriously and had been little better than assistants in spectacular uniforms. There is no doubt that this protection, alone, was a great factor in attracting the surge of trained membership to the College.

Meanwhile, if Ethel Bedford Fenwick, whose Central Committee's regulations were so acceptable, had only seen fit to agree in other ways with the College, she would have been welcomed and fully respected as one of the greatest campaigners in the nursing cause. Her life, as a result, would have been more fulfilled and indeed happier than it was destined to be.

But Mrs. Bedford Fenwick had not invented the idea of the College. Therefore she could not dominate it. The College was something which, however politely, took no cognizance of her claimed position as head of the nursing profession. Therefore she would not recognize the College until force of circumstance compelled her to do so. After which it was only to be expected (if rather tragic), that the indomitable force and stubbornness of her character made her the College's sworn enemy. Having

regard to the really great work she had done and to the fine
quality of her mind when undistracted, it is sad to have to
record that in 1926 she set to work to found a second College
of Nursing and raised a foundation for it.

*   *   *

At the meeting of 27 July 1916 the draft of the Registration
Bill to be presented to Parliament by the College of Nursing
was approved by the Council which further decided that it
should no longer be regarded as confidential. Therefore the
details of the Bill were printed as a leaflet and put on sale at
2*d.* a copy by Messrs. Eyre and Spottiswoode.

This of course was a shrewd move. Publication let the con-
tending societies know precisely where the College stood, and
also brought to the notice of all unbiassed members of Parliament the simple, practical, and straightforward points which
it asked to be ratified by law.

However, the opposition still had considerable power and
Ethel Bedford Fenwick was an indefatigable parliamentary
lobbyist—as she had the same right to be as any other Briton
who knew the technique. Publication of the leaflet therefore
was not destined to help the passage of the Bill as much as had
been hoped.

Meanwhile at that same Council meeting two very useful
donations to the College were recorded from Lord Mickleham
of 1,000 guineas and Sir Ernest Cassell, G.C.B., of £1,000. It
was also at this meeting that the grant of £300 was authorized
to establish the Scottish Board.

The immense problem of dealing fairly with all grades of
practising nurses was raised again at a Council meeting of
7 September when the following amendments were discussed
and agreed in regard to nurses who had commenced their
training sixteen years beforehand—on and after 1 January 1900.

General and civil infirmaries and hospitals were to be
recognized for training in which there were an average of
forty beds in daily occupation yearly.

In these institutions there must be a resident medical officer.

At least one course of nursing lectures must have been given
annually, followed by a qualifying examination.

Poor-law infirmaries were recognized for training in which:
there were not less than 250 beds,
a resident medical officer,
at least one annual course of lectures and a qualifying
    examination,
the training period to be not less than three years for nurses
    at a poor-law infirmary or a recognized affiliated hospital.

The College of Nursing had by its Articles of Association,
undertaken to inspect and approve hospitals for the issue of
nurse-training certificates.

The meeting closed after the agreement that there should be
one central register kept at the office of the College of Nursing
in London and that the keeping of registers of Scottish or Irish
nurses should be left to the two Boards concerned.

*   *   *

In September 1916 David Lloyd George, Secretary of State
for War, appointed a committee to consider the existing system
of obtaining nurses for the hospitals for sick and wounded
soldiers at home and abroad, and to make recommendations
for augmenting the supply. The Committee consisted of the
following members: Walter Bridgeman, M.P. (Chairman),
Viscount Knutsford, Sir Frederick Treves, Mrs. Furse, the
Hon. Francis Curzon, E. W. Morris, Capt. Harold Boulton,
and T. R. Waldron (Secretary).

At the meeting of the College of Nursing Council on the
21st the Chairman, after general discussion of the matter,
drafted the following letter to the Secretary of State for War:

'Sir,

'I beg to inform you that the Council of the College of
Nursing met this afternoon to discuss the recent appointment
of a committee . . . [as already described] . . . The Council wish
respectfully to bring to your notice the following conclusions
at which they have unanimously arrived:

(1) that the nursing profession has already responded to all
the calls that have been made upon it since the outbreak of
war and that it may, therefore, be a question whether the
appointment of such a committee is either necessary or
opportune.

(2) that the committee as announced is not such as to command the confidence of the nursing profession.

(3) that the trained nurses of the country look upon the appointment of the committee as a slight on the efforts and sacrifices they have willingly made to fulfil the requirements imposed upon the nursing staffs of military hospitals during the war.

(4) that the matrons of civil hospitals throughout the country have shown their willingness to assist the Matrons-in-Chief and the Army Nursing Board in every way, and resent the appointment of a wholly unprofessional committee to deal with this most important subject. In this connection it may be pointed out that the Army Nursing Board was set up by Royal Warrant "to act as advisers to H.M. Secretary of State in all matters pertaining to military nursing in times of peace and war".

'The Council desires to add that they have no hesitation in saying that any proposals emanating from the Army Nursing Board would receive the cordial support of the matrons of the profession at large.

'In view of this fact the Council beg that further action with regard to this committee may be suspended until the matter has had fuller consideration.'

The mood of the Council, which certainly reflected the feelings of every trained nurse, is shown by the fact that at the same time as sending the letter the Chairman also sent a notice to the Press:

'The Council of the College of Nursing met yesterday afternoon and considered the situation created by the recent appointment of a committee to deal with the supply of nurses. A letter was addressed to the Secretary of State for War expressing the hope that he would suspend any further action in connection with the committee until fuller consideration.'

This direct attack backed up by the sharp comment which followed from the national Press had its effect. The Committee was forthwith enlarged by the co-option of two Matrons-in-Chief and seven members of the College of Nursing Council.

This was a double triumph, first of course since it brought the expertise of professionalism to an otherwise unqualified membership, but second because it proved to the profession that the College of Nursing had 'arrived'.

The Council had been quick to take up its first public issue; it had fearlessly criticized the action of one of the most powerful Ministers in the Government—and it had won its point.

CHAPTER EIGHT

The Nurses Act, 1919

THE COLLEGE OF NURSING LIMITED started its separate working life in small offices in Vere Street, London, W.1 in which Mary Rundle, Gertrude Cowlin, and the staff laboured all hours laying the foundations of the first organization.

Meanwhile both the College Council and that of the Royal British Nurses Association had seen that advantages for both would lie in amalgamation. In the Second Annual Report of the College of Nursing Ltd., paragraph 8 states:

'Recognizing the identity of many of the aims of the Royal British Nurses Association with those of the College, and the advantages which would accrue to the latter body by associating itself with a Corporation already possessing a Royal Charter, the Council early entered into negotiations . . . with a view to amalgamation under the title of the "Royal British College of Nursing" . . .'

The Council had, in fact, drafted an agreement to this end together with a Supplemental Charter and Bye-laws which had been fully approved by the R.B.N.A., at a General Meeting in January 1917. The new Charter was forthwith placed before the Privy Council and it seemed that a favourable decision would not long be delayed. The Councils of both bodies realized that amalgamation would put them in a strong position to present a Registration Bill, and had already agreed that the first National Register thereunder would be formed from the joint roll of membership of the College and the R.B.N.A.

It was this which gave Arthur Stanley reason to report to the College Council that he hoped shortly to have good news on the subject. However the issue was almost immediately baulked by a petition against the amalgamation lodged by the Society for the State Registration of Trained Nurses, the Central Committee of which was dominated by the Nurse Secretary—Mrs. Bedford Fenwick.

Then Sir Almeric Fitzroy, the Clerk to the Privy Council, wrote to say that one or two amendments would have to be made to the proposed Supplemental Charter. In the main these concerned the use of the words 'official Register' where this had been proposed, and the undertaking to give nurses protection thereunder.

Both these items he very rightly pointed out could only be made effectual by Acts of Parliament which the King, in granting a Charter, could not anticipate. Sir Almeric, however, added his own suggestion for alternative phrases (meaning practically the same things) which would obviate the difficulties.

To such practical men as Stanley and Cooper Perry these alterations were trivial and they were prepared to accept Sir Almeric's expert help without question. But in September 1917 they were astounded to receive a letter from the R.B.N.A. which stated that the Council thereof, after considering Sir Almeric's amendments, 'have reluctantly come to the conclusion that it would not be to the interest of the Corporation to accept the alterations suggested'.

The College of Nursing replied that the amendments made no practical difference to the position and asked for further enlightenment. But in a dilatory correspondence it emerged that the R.B.N.A. was backing out of the proposed amalgamation.

This was a ridiculous situation since Princess Christian, the prized Royal Patron of the R.B.N.A., when told of the proposal had announced:

'Should a satisfactory scheme of union between the College of Nursing and the R.B.N.A. be formulated H.R.H. the Princess would be disposed to accept a position of honour in the conjoint Society.' And further: 'The fusion of the two bodies can and will be of the greatest advantage to both the Nursing Profession at large and the public generally.'

Although Ethel Bedford Fenwick was at the time virtually not on speaking terms with her own creation, the R.B.N.A., she must have found the Royal pronouncement somewhat galling. The Princess, indeed, was by no means to be the only Royal personage who had sound common sense and was prepared to voice it, as we of this generation know well.

Nor was she to be the only one to be flatly disregarded. The R.B.N.A. appeared for a while to be interested in fusion, but the interest waned—probably because the College membership was well over 13,000 while their own (never officially disclosed) was at its best very much less. Although Arthur Stanley had clearly offered them an equal share in control it seems that they had heard about he who went for a ride on a tiger. In any case nothing was done and at last the College realized that unless some sort of spur was applied nothing further was likely to be done. A letter was therefore despatched to the R.B.N.A. which left nothing to the imagination.

Its impact lay in the paragraph:

'It was undoubtedly of some importance to the College of Nursing in its early days to seek to ally itself with your Association, just as it was of importance for your Association to obtain enlarged powers, the new infusion of energy, and increased membership, which would have come about by the establishment of the amalgamated bodies as the Royal British College of Nursing: but as the College of Nursing has now become well known, and as an appeal for funds . . . has met with the widest reception by the Press and public, the advantage to the College becomes less obvious.'

Like many another kindly man Stanley could produce a biting touch of sarcasm when seriously annoyed. The attitude of the R.B.N.A. and the shilly-shallying was upsetting carefully laid plans, so that the time had come for the Association to throw in its lot with the prospering College or to go its own way and have done. As might be expected it did neither but sought to temporise, still.

This was enough for Stanley, however. He dismissed the R.B.N.A. from his forward plans as from that moment although he allowed polite exchanges to continue. Privately, he determined that the College must gain a Royal Charter independently, although he knew well enough the difficulties that would arise.

Meanwhile, just as he had suspected, the College was notified in November that the R.B.N.A. General Council had decided not to proceed with their application for the grant of a Supplemental Charter and had informed the Privy Council of that fact.

The reply from the College rather naturally protested at the pointless and dilatory manner in which the R.B.N.A. had at last arrived at this conclusion. This provoked an angry answer in which the R.B.N.A. announced that the modified Supplemental Charter had granted them no further powers than those they already possessed.

Stanley let it go at that. By the terms of the original agreement to amalgamate, neither side had asked or expected wider powers. The R.B.N.A. had been offered equal representation in a body which would increase its membership many times over by a stroke of the pen; in return the College of Nursing Limited was to receive only the change of title to The Royal British College of Nursing. The benefit of such a conjoint body to the nursing profession and to the public was obvious, as would have been its greatly enhanced power in Parliamentary negotiation for a National Register.

Stanley, however, merely replied that he hoped the R.B.N.A. would forward all the correspondence on the subject to the Press, as he proposed to do, in order that the public and the profession could make their own judgement. Obviously this hurt, for a final, angry letter was received in which the R.B.N.A. went into a detailed (but somewhat unconvincing) self-justification and imperiously demanded that Sir Stanley should include this effusion with whatever he was forwarding to the Press.

Which he did. And thereupon dropped the matter from his mind.

Meanwhile discussions had continued with the Central Committee for the State Registration of Nurses but common ground could not yet be found.* The Central Committee still demanded College agreement to certain amendments. Shorn of legal circumlocution these were:

(1) that the General Nursing Council to be appointed by the Bill should number fifteen each from the College and the Central Committee plus two appointed by the Privy Council, three by Local Government Boards, three by the British Medical Association, six by nurse-training schools and one by the Medico-Psychological Association.

(2) (and onwards) various alterations in standards required in hospitals entitled to issue certificates.

These amendments had been presented to the meeting of the College Council in October 1916 in the form of a letter signed by Ethel Bedford Fenwick as Hon. Nurse Secretary of the Central Committee. The letter in reply drafted by Stanley was bland reasonableness. He had written:

'Dear Madam,
'. . . I write with the greater readiness as I feel that the differences between us are matters rather of expediency and policy than of fundamental principles. Both parties are out for State Registration; it is merely a question how to get it with a minimum of friction and delay.

'To consider the amendments of your Committee to the Fourth draft of the College of Nursing Bill *seriatim:*

[On the composition of the First General Nursing Council under the Act]: 'The Central Committee excludes names and suggests a list of appointing bodies.

(1) The Central Committee suggests no representation of Poor Law authorities or Poor Law nurses.

(2) No representation of Scotland or Ireland.

(3) There will be difficulty in choosing six out of the whole of the nurse-training schools without exciting jealousy among the excluded.

'On behalf of the (College) Council's proposal to set out the names of the First General Nursing Council I urge:

* See p. 40

(1) that it is more difficult in Parliament to object to names of individuals than to a list of nominating bodies.

(2) that Members are more likely to view favourably a Bill for Registration if they know of whom the First General Nursing Council is actually to consist, than if they are asked to entrust nomination of it to bodies of whom they know little or nothing.

'. . . I ought perhaps to repeat that . . . the Central Committee which has done so much to establish registration for nurses should have as many nominees on the First Council as the College has.

'. . . I fancy that if we once got to work round a table many of the difficulties anticipated would be found practically to solve themselves and that we could get out a Council which would command the confidence of the Profession, of the public and of the Houses of Parliament.'

The letter was long and detailed, pointing out the differences between the two Bodies' suggestions, and suggesting compromise on many points.

It concluded:

'. . . the Council of the College has been strongly advised by its Solicitors and Parliamentary Counsel to lighten the Bill as much as possible by confining the provisions to main principles rather than to elaborate details, and the main principle we are interested in is that nurses should appoint two-thirds of the Permanent Council, and this is laid down in Clause 4(1)(a).

'The proportionate representation of other interests may very well be left, I think, to the First Council. The attempt to define how it should be done in the Bill, itself, would almost certainly lead to trouble, and might even be fatal to the measure.

'. . . there is absolutely no hope of presenting a contentious Bill in the present state of public business; therefore an agreed measure is the only chance we have of obtaining the State recognition of the nursing profession . . . I hope that the explanations I have given of our Bill may convince your Committee that, as I said at the beginning of this letter, our differences concern details not fundamentals and consequently ought not to be incapable of mutual adjustment.'

For once Stanley had made a misjudgement. The points he had put forward were fair, clear, balanced, and carefully worked-out for the benefit of nurses as a whole. Although he had good reason to know Ethel Bedford Fenwick as a woman of grim stubbornness, he genuinely believed that—since they were both working for the same fundamentals—his letter would bring her and her delegates back to the table. If they were prepared to discuss and concede he knew the College Council would meet them half way at almost all points.

Parliament was occupied with the war, then in one of its most dangerous and critical stages. All the fierce behind-the-scenes jockeying and arguing that precedes a change of Prime Minister was at its height. David Lloyd George was about to supplant Herbert Asquith and the Parliamentary atmosphere was highly charged. The House would certainly be willing to pass a measure that everyone concerned agreed upon, but it would not brook discussion of what in the circumstances it would regard as trivialities.

Stanley felt so confident that after he had offered the College Council his letter to Ethel Bedford Fenwick for approval (which it received) he said that shortly he hoped to place before the Council certain documents on the proposed agreement between the College and the Central Committee.

But Ethel Bedford Fenwick was angry and, magnificent warrior that she was, her anger meant planning and action, not just a letting off of fireworks. She returned a cold reply in October 1916, stating that her Committee 'had no further jurisdiction' to discuss matters. And would he say whether or not his unofficial letter was to be regarded as the official view of the College Council. To this Stanley made the obvious reply in the politest terms, but he now realized that there would be little hope of bringing Ethel Bedford Fenwick, or any who owed her allegiance, to cool discussion.

During the months that followed the draft College Bill was further amended to take account of various points that had been put forward by those interested in supporting state registration. In the following May (1917) Ethel Bedford Fenwick invited nurses to sign a petition to be presented to the Prime Minister urging that any Bill for State Registration should set out the names of the various organized nurses' societies for appointing representatives to the Provisional Council. As this was one of the main points of contention between the College and the Central Committee, the College sent out a memorandum to its members which set out the whole position and advised members not to sign but to leave the Council and the College 'free to promote its Bill for the State Registration of Nurses in whatever form may seem most likely to conduce its speedy acceptance by Parliament'.

The protracted negotiations with the Royal British Nurses Association regarding amalgamation* had delayed the work of the College in presenting a Bill to Parliament, as the Council felt that the final details should be decided by the Council of the amalgamated body. These negotiations finally broke down towards the end of 1917 and early in 1918 the College made a further approach to the Central Committee as it considered that the need for a Parliamentary Bill to establish nursing as a registered profession, and to regularise training and certification, was greater than smaller details which might well be adjusted in the committee stages. In July 1918 the Central Committee was notified that the College Council was prepared to withdraw almost all the College's objections set forth in Stanley's letter to Mrs. Bedford Fenwick. The only point upon which the Council would not give way was the demand by the College that two-thirds of the members of the General Nursing Council (to be set up under the Bill) should be directly elected by nurses on the Register.

Possibly because Ethel Bedford Fenwick realized that those on the College Register would already enormously outnumber those on the Registers of all other Nursing Societies, she—or her Committee, officially—would not agree to this. The effort to arrange an agreed Bill continued throughout the year but in December 1918 the Central Committee notified the College that they had, in the interim, drafted their own measure which they regarded as being 'a far better Bill than that proposed by the College of Nursing Ltd.' Accordingly they were going to present it to Parliament forthwith. Stanley would still have made a gesture of give and take had it been possible, but he

* See pp. 48-51.

5

saw in the Central Committee's Bill that eleven places on the proposed General Nursing Council were allotted to the R.B.N.A., and only four to the College in spite of the fact that the College by that time had swept to the immense success of an over thirteen thousand membership—at a reasonable estimate more than four times that of the R.B.N.A.

Since the Central Committee would not even discuss the matter there was only one course left—the Committee's Bill was presented early in 1919 and so was that of the College of Nursing.

Fortunately, at that time, the newly created Ministry of Health (previously a Local Government Department) had as its first head an able and outstanding administrator, Dr. (later Viscount) Christopher Addison, already well versed in the antagonisms that had bedevilled all attempts to organize nursing. He also owned a sense of humour, so that when faced with the details of the two contentious Bills he figuratively threw his hands in the air, ordered both to be removed from his sight, and announced that he would draft a Bill for the purpose himself.

This, in fact, Dr. Addison did without delay, keeping clearly in mind the most practical and commonsense items in both measures. As a result the Nurses Act finally received the Royal Assent and passed into law on 23 December 1919, containing the provisions for training and registration already agreed between the two main bodies, but most important, the requirement insisted upon by the College against all opposition that a minimum of two-thirds of the General Nursing Council be democratically elected by nurses on the national Register.

CHAPTER NINE

The First General Nursing Council

EARLY IN 1920 the Minister invited the College to suggest names of its representatives for the first General Nursing Council and these, true to principle, the College obtained by postal vote from the nurses on its own Register. The elected were Miss Cox-Davies, Miss Lloyd Still, and Miss Sparshott.

By the terms of the Act a General Nursing Council for England and Wales was established with the duty to form and keep a register of nurses for the sick consisting of the following parts:

A general part containing the names of all nurses qualifying according to details to be laid down by the General Nursing Council.

A supplementary part containing the names of male nurses.

A supplementary part containing the names of mental nurses.

A supplementary part for nurses trained in the nursing of sick children.

All rules concerning training qualification and admission to the Register had to be approved by the Minister of Health and there were also details for the registration of 'existing nurses' who had been in practice for a minimum of three years prior to November 1919, and whom the G.N.C. regarded as 'having adequate knowledge and experience of the nursing of the sick'.

And finally there were penalties for any who unlawfully assumed the title of 'Registered Nurse' or gave false information in applying for registration.

Similar Acts were shortly passed to the same general effect to cover Scotland and Ireland.

These Acts of 1919, so much the result of work by the College of Nursing, formed the most important measures for the protection of the public from the ignorant and untrained, and also put the nursing profession for the first time upon a proper basis of training and qualification.

The passing of the Acts was a triumph for the College, for common sense and democratic method against that of autocracy. It is, however, pleasing to record that the indomitable spirit of Ethel Bedford Fenwick was above recognition of defeat. A battle for nursing had been won; therefore as self-ordained (and to a great extent deserved) head of the nursing profession, the victory must be hers, alone.

In her *British Journal of Nursing* there appeared later in a leading article:

'When we come to consider the claims of candidates for election to the General Nursing Council the name that will come first in everyone's thoughts must be that of Mrs. Bedford Fenwick for, without this forceful, indomitable worker and brilliant organizer the nurses of the United Kingdom would have no Nursing Act and it is a matter of *noblesse oblige* that whoever is . . . returned to the Council in the coming election Mrs. Fenwick is placed there with all honour . . .'

Noblesse oblige was observed by Dr. Addison who, quite rightly and fairly, nominated her to the Council for England and Wales. The Council members, too conscious of the great work she had done to allow other matters to influence them, elected her Chairman of the Registration Committee.

The strength of the College was marked in the composition of the General Nursing Council. Two members to represent the public were named by the Privy Council and two by the Board of Education. Five were medical men or specialists. Nine of the sixteen nursing members were appointed from the College of Nursing to four from the R.B.N.A. The remainder were from Poor Law infirmaries or were hospital matrons.

In its early days, however, the General Nursing Council was in troubled waters. At first it laid down that one year's training in a hospital approved by the Council must be the qualification for an 'existing nurse'. But there was a general outcry against this and the College objected with good reason because 'it was unfair to admit a woman with one year's training at a tiny hospital and two years' practice, and to refuse a woman with a shorter training and nineteen years' practice'.

It was further realised that the General Council's rule would render quite a number of very senior members of the profession in high positions ineligible for registration.

It was useless for Ethel Bedford Fenwick to fulminate in her *British Journal of Nursing* that the Register would be 'flooded with V.A.D.s, Village Nurses and Cottage Nurses who have shirked training'. She was crying out against the reality that it was impossible at that time for all the hospitals in the country and all the sick who needed care to be provided with trained nurses. In the years to come that could—and would—be achieved by a gradual amending and tightening-up of the rules affecting nurse training, and by the fact that the untrained nurses in practice would leave this world at the end of their allotted spans.

Parliament, therefore, over-rode the General Nursing Council and passed the following measure—nurses could be admitted to the Register who could present:

(1) a certificate of good character.

(2) a certificate signed by the matron of a general hospital or an infirmary, or by two medical men setting out that the applicant has been in attendance upon the sick in the capacity of a nurse for a period of not less than three years prior to 1 November 1919; and

(3) a certificate signed by a registered nurse and two medical men, one of whom shall be on the staff of a general hospital, setting out that the applicant has adequate knowledge and experience of medical and surgical nursing and is competent to attend upon the sick in the capacity of a nurse.

The other immediate problem the General Nursing Council had to face was concerned with the details of training and the approval of training schools. With Parliamentary approval, the Council ordained that nurses not at that time yet in practice should only be registered if they had received the form of training approved by the Council at a training school which it had approved. Since one of its main duties was to improve standards of nursing, this meant careful attention to details of training. But if it withheld its approval of a training school the hospital concerned still had, under the Act, the right of appeal to the Minister of Health. This was repeatedly used and on more than one occasion the Minister, having regard to the shortage, reversed the Council's decision.

Naturally the result was to make the Council over-cautious, but such forcible restraint went against the grain with its members who knew that many hospitals regarded probationers as convenient cheap labour, and would not go to the effort or expense of giving them any real training. Probably the greatest of the Council's difficulties was that it had, as a body, to do all its own inspecting of training schools. This was work which could well have been carried out by a paid staff of sister status and experience. It was uneconomic and often unworkable for the task to be covered by matron members of the Council whose available spare time was limited. This was eventually put right and inspectors appointed, but in the early days it multiplied the general difficulties.

There was also much controversy about the form of training and finally, after Parliamentary pressure, the Council announced that its syllabus of training should be advisory 'in the hope that it may aid the training schools in arriving at a general standard of nursing education'.

There were many more small than large hospitals serving the population, and it was obvious that small hospitals would have more difficulty in giving adequate training than the larger and more lavishly equipped hospitals. But at that time the small ones were far shorter of nurses than the large ones, and a rigid syllabus of compulsory training would have made their case even more difficult.

It will be remembered, of course, that entry to the Register of the College of Nursing was entirely different and on the basis of a minimum three years' training certificated by an approved school. This was eventually altered (in 1923) when the College amended its rules and admitted all general trained nurses who were registered by the G.N.C.

In the meantime Ethel Bedford Fenwick had found herself at cross-purposes with her colleagues on the General Nursing

Council. To give her complete and unbiassed justice, perhaps it is best to tell about what happened in her own words, given in her election address, at the elections to the General Nursing Council for England and Wales in 1922:

'. . . Elected as Chairman of the Registration Committee I helped to draft the rules including those for the honourable conduct of business . . . They proved too just, and it was found that . . . a certain minority of the Council including myself must be removed from power. How, by a secret attack on me at the Ministry of Health this was done, how the rules were altered and thrust through Parliament is now a part of history . . .'

Ethel Bedford Fenwick was elected Chairman of the Registration sub-committee, and the Register was opened in November 1921. To deal with the detail work a Registrar was appointed who would, in the normal way of such things, have dealt with the clerkly work of checking minutae of applications. In this case, however, the Chairman for her own reasons personally examined every individual certificate, cross-questioned the Registrar upon her investigations, and so held up the work that a large backlog of applications soon began to accumulate. In less than half a year about 3,500 applications were received but under 1,000 were dealt with.

It seemed to the General Nursing Council that Mrs. Bedford Fenwick was either obstructing operations or was determined to 'run' the organization by her domination of the Registration sub-committee. The majority of the members (sixteen including the Chairman) took the only course, and resigned. This of course immediately came to the notice of the Minister of Health who persuaded them to resume their duties by promising a revision of Mrs. Bedford Fenwick's rules, so that only doubtful cases should be checked by the sub-committee.

This was held by Mrs. Bedford Fenwick to be a 'secret attack' upon her. When the first democratic election to the General Nursing Council was held she lost her seat although she fought the campaign fiercely. Her 'removal from power' was by the free vote of the registered nurses, not by the action of the Minister or anyone else.

To be candid this was a matter of relief to those with whom she had been working who were members of her *bête noire*, the College of Nursing; relief—but certainly not pleasure, because it was tragic to see such a magnificent and gifted character defeated by misapplication of her own strength.

The date set for the closing of the Register for 'existing nurses' was 14 July 1923. By that time over 40,000 of the 70,000 believed to be in practice had applied. This was as fair a proportion as might have been expected since there were still in the depths of the country 'existing nurses' who were, at best, semi-literate and did not bother themselves with reading either the national or nursing Press. It was rather charmingly feminine that the great rush for registration came at almost the last—over 12,000 in the final six weeks and over 1,000 on the last day.

Although the General Nursing Council had originally intended that after that date only those nurses who had received three years' training at an approved training school under a syllabus laid down by the Council and had passed the Council's examination should be admitted to the Register, the syllabus drawn up by the Council was persistently opposed by the Minister. It was therefore not until 1925 when, as has been said, the Council agreed to make the syllabus advisory only, that the first state examination was held. The closing date for registration of existing nurses was also extended until 1925.

National Registration came at last to success through intense striving by both right-headed, and well-meaning wrong-headed people; it survived its first months of existence by a mixture of casuistry, compromise, retreat from idealism, and hard common sense—in which it differed little from many another movement which has eventually gained the respect of the world. It grew and developed by the sheer hard work of those who have formed the General Nursing Council from that day to this.

Registered nurses however were finding that their registration got them no higher rates and no preference in employment, so naturally they were vocal in asking what was the use of the Council? For obvious political reasons the Government which was responsible for the passing of the Act would not empower the Ministry of Health to demand that hospitals or Local Authorities should employ only Registered nurses, and of course this reduced the value of state registration in general estimation.

The Government's obvious difficulty in this was that it dared not deny employment to thousands of 'practising nurses' all over the country who had not bothered to register —who probably could not have produced even the basic 'qualifications' demanded—but who now held the women's vote. . . .

However the authorities who mattered—the Local Authorities, hospital managements, and District Nursing Associations —not only accepted the necessity of registration, but were ruling that only Registered nurses should form their staffs. The problem that followed this was a shortage of Registered nurses in all but the best-paid, most congenial and 'higher status' forms of the work.

The larger hospitals in London and the greater cities were never short nor was district nursing. The older and semi-trained 'nurses in practice' were generally content to do private domiciliary work and to staff nursing homes and convalescent homes.

The problem of nursing recruitment was only likely to be solved by a seemingly impossible increase in pay-rates and by hard persuasion of hospitals to modify some of their more pointlessly harsh disciplinary rules.

CHAPTER TEN

V.A.D.

MEMBERS OF the Voluntary Aid Detachments have already been mentioned in passing. This was an organization which had been formed by a joint committee of the Order of St. John of Jerusalem and the British Red Cross Society as far back as 1909. Although St. Thomas's Hospital later gave members a very short semi-training, they were for the most part completely untrained, and the idea behind their embodiment had been that they should take the place of orderlies in the Royal Army Medical Corps in hospitals in the case of war.

A very different situation developed. The V.A.D. girls came from better-off families and included a number of young women of title including, for a while, the much publicized Lady Diana Manners. Many of them were employed after the outbreak of war in mansion-hospitals specially converted for the nursing of wounded officers. They all wore a red cross upon the apron-bosom and upon the uniform cap, and naturally (because of their social background) they were much photographed and belauded in the general and pictorial Press.

Equally naturally, they were not loved by the mass of experienced, really hard-working nurses who had little chance of (and in most cases no desire for) employment in the private hospitals run by titled dowagers. Even so, in justice to the V.A.D.s, a large proportion of them did useful work throughout the war, but it was an age in which snobbery was an accepted condition of life and many of them (usually those with the least claim to gentility) allowed it to be known that they did not consider themselves to be on a level with 'ordinary nurses'. They were, of course, right, but not quite in the way they imagined.

In short they were thoroughly and very understandably

unpopular with the nursing profession, and when the war ended many of the qualified nurses had reason to suspect that the V.A.D.s would be competing with them unfairly in the professional employment market.

It was said that Arthur Stanley was secretly trying to get untrained V.A.D.s admitted to College membership because so many of them had good social background.

A large number of people believed this, largely because people in general are more inclined to believe a rumour than to take the simple course of going to the right source and reading simple facts. If they had applied to the College the efficient and dedicated Miss Rundle would have forthwith provided the truth as set out in Stanley's own statements. But few did.

Naturally, trained nurses and nurses in practice who had learned their business by doing it for many years were resentful because Dr. Addison, the Minister of Health, had added to their fears by announcing: 'We shall need many more nurses than we have ever had before, and we are fortunate in having . . . thousands of women who have gained experience in V.A.D. work.'

Then the Government announced a Nurses' Demobilization and Resettlement Committee which, while it was for the benefit of all nurses, also made the point that ex-V.A.D.s were to receive some sort of training. The result was that Stanley, by reason of his known connection with the Red Cross Society (part-founders of the V.A.D.) was believed to be playing a double game.

Nothing was further from the truth. Stanley had stated in public: 'Our (the College's) endeavour will be to draw a clear line between trained nurses and V.A.D.s and to encourage such of the latter who are suitable to obtain the three years' certificate from a general hospital, which will enable them to become members of the College of Nursing.'

Both Arthur Stanley and Cooper Perry realized that the real position concerning V.A.D.s was not clearly known by the majority of qualified nurses. One obvious result of the war was that several million men—boy-friends and husbands—had been killed. Another result was that money had changed hands with violent effect as between social classes. A good number of people had made fortunes but a vast number had lost calamitously. All over the country 'comfortably off' families of 1913 were finding by 1919 that they had little or nothing. Their daughters had now to earn a living, and owing to the enormous casualty rate of the war, had infinitely less chance of marriage.

It was from these classes, the middle and upper middle, who had suffered most financially from war, that most of the V.A.D.s came. The majority of them who now faced earning their bread had only what half-skill they had learned in war hospitals to bring to the market. They were genuinely in need of help, and the Government realized it and proposed a scheme to help them train fully.

Arthur Stanley had spoken with great care on the subject. He had proposed that only 'such of them who are suitable' should be trained further. There were left the large number who could never be turned into good nurses, as he knew in common with anyone else of hospital experience. For these, through the Red Cross, Arthur Stanley suggested a scheme which he felt would not only be workable and just, but which would not arouse the opposition of qualified nurses. He outlined the plan: '. . . in every village a proper system under which V.A.D.s, trained in home nursing and first aid, could work. They could perfectly well do all the small things such as attending to cuts and the like.' In this sort of work he pointed out that it would be uneconomic to employ fully trained nurses who would be wasting most of their skill and time.

In addition to this Stanley, in his negotiations with the R.B.N.A., had agreed without question that untrained V.A.D.s should *not* be admitted to either of their Registers or the National Register.

In spite of all this Mrs. Bedford Fenwick blandly accused Stanley of proposing to push V.A.D.s into positions which should be reserved for trained nurses. Naturally, since her accusation was published in the columns of her *British Journal of Nursing*, there were many who believed it.

However, the truth eventually prevailed by the unexpected —but what should have been obvious—help of the V.A.D.s themselves. They applied in large numbers for registration at the College, but found that the rule was being rigidly maintained. Only a three-year certificate of training from an approved hospital could gain them membership.

Naturally, they talked about it. Naturally, they reviled the College and all its works. In which they did the College a most valuable good turn, for the talk spread as talk always does, and wherever it spread it brought full confidence in the College among all the qualified and practising nurses and nurses in training for whom it had been founded.

CHAPTER ELEVEN

The Cowdray Gift

As HAS already been stated one of the main aims of the College on its foundation was to secure the state registration of nurses. It was envisaged that the College would become the official registering body and that its roll of membership would form the first part of the State Register. When, subsequently, it became clear that a separate body, the General Nursing Council, was to be established under the 1919 Act charged with the duty of keeping a Register of Nurses it had been hoped that members of the College would automatically be accepted for registration without further question. Members on joining the College had therefore been charged a registration fee of one guinea.

When, under the rules laid down by the first Council it was announced that all nurses wishing to register, including members of the College, would have to apply to and pay a registration fee to the General Nursing Council, the College offered to refund to members the full guinea registration fee paid or such part of it as would be required to pay the State Registration fee. While a few members of the College availed themselves of this offer the majority did not do so, realizing that the work of the College could not be carried on without adequate funds.

One of the main concerns of the Council of the College since its inception was to keep its members informed of the work being undertaken on their behalf and to provide an opportunity for members to express their views. Towards the end of 1919 therefore the Council decided to publish a Quarterly Bulletin which for the first year would be issued free to members (6d. to non-members). The first Bulletin appeared in January 1920. By the Annual General Meeting of that year it had become clear that with the developing work of the College including the cost of the Bulletin a regular annual income was essential. It was

therefore proposed at that meeting that the Articles of Association should be amended to allow an annual subscription being
paid by its members. The meeting showed that it fully appreciated all that the College had done and was doing for nurses by
supporting the proposal.

At an Extraordinary General Meeting in November 1920
resolutions amending the Articles of Association were adopted
as a result of which members joining the College after
20 November 1920 were required to pay an entrance fee of
one guinea and an annual subscription of 'not more than
twenty shillings', as the Council might from time to time
appoint. In fact the subscription laid down at that time by the
Council was only five shillings.

Those members of the College, some 19,500 of them, who
had joined before November 1920 could not of course be asked
to pay an annual subscription, although very many of them
voluntarily did so. Known as the 'Founder Members', they
were the backbone of the College in its early days. It was their
devotion and their work all over the country which had ensured
the College's success. It was their dedication to all that the
College stood for which helped to raise the Endowment and
the Tribute Funds, and it must not be forgotten that the guinea
they paid then was worth in purchasing power some eight times
what it is today; moreover their salaries were disproportionately
lower.

Towards the end of 1917 the British Women's Hospital
Committee had launched the 'Nation's Fund For Nurses'. The
object of this was to raise two funds: one a Tribute Fund, the
income from the invested capital to be used to help nurses
broken in health as a result of their war service; the other an
Endowment Fund for the College of Nursing. The target for
each fund was set at £100,000. The Committee recognized
that if it waited until the full sum for the Tribute Fund was
collected, many nurses in need would inevitably suffer. A
special committee of six members nominated by the British
Women's Hospital Committee and six by the College was
therefore set up under the Chairmanship of Lady Cowdray to
meet these needs as they arose. Subsequently the Tribute
Fund which reached its target first was incorporated as the

Nation's Fund for Nurses and still today does valuable work in assisting nurses in need.

A suggestion that members themselves should bring the Endowment Fund up to its target by each collecting £2. 10s. was taken up with enthusiasm. Many and varied were the schemes thought up by members for raising this sum in order that their College might be adequately endowed. The names of all those who contributed this amount, or more, were subsequently inscribed on vellum in a beautifully bound volume and each was presented with a small silver key.

Some very generous gifts to the Welfare Fund were received, notably one from Sir John and Lady Martin-Harvey which, with other contributions including one of £4,000 from the British Farmers Association, was used to buy a charmingly situated house to be used as a rest home at Bonchurch, Isle of Wight, where convalescent nurses might recuperate. This became a favourite place of call with Queen Mary in the summer months when the King was occupied with his favourite sport of sailing. The Queen liked nothing better than a cup of tea and an informal chat with people she respected and who knew what they were talking about.

The greatest charm of the Queen's character was her genuine compassion for any form of human affliction. Unheralded as her visits were, they were never publicized in any way unless she was present on an official occasion. One morning during Cowes Week—probably when the very 'blue-water' King was taking his yacht out in turbulent weather—the Queen had herself driven across to the Bonchurch Rest Home, but found when she had reached the entrance that only an astonished and scared kitchen-maid was to be seen.

'Is Miss Burgess in?' asked the Queen, smiling to relieve the girl's obvious near-panic.

'Yes'm,' gasped the girl. 'But—y'majesty she'm upstairs.'

'Then could you ask her to step down, please?'

The girl hesitated.

'Yes'm, but—but she'm a cryin'. 'Er little 'arg just died, and she's took it that bad——'

The Queen moved impulsively. 'Where is her room?' she asked. 'I must see her at once.'

But as she reached the stairs, Miss Burgess, the Matron, came hurrying down. She was red-eyed and frantically trying to tidy her hair, having, at the last moment, noticed the Royal car at the door. Naturally, she began trying to apologize but the Queen took her by the arm and guided her to the sitting-room. 'We must have a cup of tea, and you must tell me all about it,' she said, her own eyes suspiciously bright. 'Losing a pet is losing a loved friend. Now let us sit down together.'

And with all the unaffected sympathy to be expected of a friendly next-door neighbour the Queen sat, her hand on Miss Burgess's arm, comforting her for the next half-hour.

In January 1919 the College of Nursing moved into much larger and better appointed premises at No. 7 Henrietta Street (later to be renamed Henrietta Place), Cavendish Square. Here, after a certain amount of alteration and renovation, space was found for the London Local Centre, and there were of course club-rooms, committee rooms, and offices for the day-to-day business.

In much of this Gertrude Cowlin was the energetic prime mover. She had by that time already initiated nineteen local centres in various parts of the country, most of which had their own club-rooms in which post-graduate lectures were held as well as social occasions. The extraordinary variety of work she undertook for the College is detailed elsewhere,* but the widespread organization of the branches as it is today, owes its existence to her driving energy and foresight in the first place.

By 1921, however, this accommodation, although incomparably better than that at Vere Street, was already proving too cramped to house the growing commitments of the Council and staff. A new headquarters was needed for an administrative organization that was bound to be increased with a rapidly increasing membership.

In 1921 Rachael Cox-Davies had already discussed this with her colleagues on the Council. Her dream—vision is perhaps a better word—was an entirely new College building designed for its purpose. Until finances would permit of such a thing with a comfortable margin the Council, naturally, could not

* See pp. 38–39.

6

seriously consider the idea. But although it had to be shelved for the time being, the Council, in considering the future, believed that any new building should be as centrally placed, when it should materialize, as the present headquarters. In short, it was better to rub along in the present central position, however cramped, than think of migrating to the suburbs in search of cheap land.

Rachael Cox-Davies had no love of 'rubbing along' in any circumstances. She was mercurially Welsh and firmly believed in her own sixth sense of 'feeling' how to handle any situation. Once she had an idea, she could not forget it until it had been made reality—and the idea of a central College building with all the dignity of impressive architecture was firmly planted in her mind.

At that period Lady Cowdray, who had been interested in the college for several years, had also taken an active part in raising money for the Nation's Fund for Nurses: In 1920 she had provided two Sister Tutor Studentships for College members, and in 1921 was elected to the Council of the College. Rachael Cox-Davies decided to interest her further. The Cowdray fortune was great, but Miss Cox-Davies knew that rich people usually have a very acute sense of the value of money, from which they are not easily parted. However, she also knew Lady Cowdray as a woman of generous instincts as well as high intelligence. Friendship between them developed, and there came an afternoon when Lady Cowdray was to leave England on holiday. Rachael Cox-Davies volunteered to see her off at the station, and joined her in the taxi-cab.

In the ten minutes that followed, and with the prospect of her companion being out of reach for the next three months, Miss Cox-Davies consulted her intuition. She decided that the moment had come; and that it was a propitious moment. As the taxi approached Victoria Station she referred briefly to what she had already mentioned that day—the rocketing membership figure, and the need for a larger headquarters. Then, inwardly tensing herself, she asked her companion if she would give the College a new building—and made the request outwardly with the ease that she might have asked for a two-guinea subscription. Lady Cowdray agreed to the request without the slightest hesitation. She did not ask what the cost might be or for any further detail.

The cab arrived at the station, and in the ensuing bustle and final farewells Rachael Cox-Davies was far too wise to say anything more on the subject. She knew her companion, and had not the slightest doubt that the brief promise would be fulfilled.

It was. Lady Cowdray bought the mansion standing on the corner of Henrietta Place and Cavendish Square which had been the London home of Prime Minister Herbert Asquith and his equally famous wife 'Margot'. This was renovated into a residential club for nurses and professional women which is now famous as the Cowdray Club. The garden of the Club had a frontage on to Henrietta Place and it was here that Lady Cowdray built the new College headquarters. Later on in the 'thirties she bought the properties between, which were pulled down and rebuilt completely to form the College of Nursing and the Library of Nursing, all the three buildings being made inter-connecting.

Rachael Cox-Davies' Welsh intuition was vindicated; Lady Cowdray's taxi-fare might perhaps be regarded as high since the fullness of her benefactions to the College were destined to reach some half-million pounds. It is pleasant to record, however, that the whole project was obviously a labour of love to her from the start.

One lady—who had something of a queenly spirit—was most definitely *not* amused by these events. Ethel Bedford Fenwick's *British Journal of Nursing*, in announcing the Cowdray gift, first of all decried the raising of funds for the College from the public: '. . . begging for them [the nurses] from all and sundry through the Nation's Fund, arousing bitter indignation and resentment.' (Which seems a little peculiar since a large proportion of hospital nursing was then supported by voluntary contributions, widely solicited.) But the *Journal* continued: 'But when wealth is accumulated through commerce and the labour of thousands of manual workers it is only just that some of it should be returned to them by mercantile millionaires. The higher education of trained nurses will, let us hope, be a means through which the health of people will surely benefit.

It is to be regretted that the endowment of the College of Nursing Ltd. did not take place four years ago, when the self-respecting section of the nursing profession might have been spared all the humiliation consequent upon the touting and degrading press campaign made in its name by persons of wealth lacking in sensibility.'

The last, somewhat ill-tempered line, was prompted by the fact that Lady Cowdray had been active in the promotion and running of the Nation's Fund for Nurses.

The fine new building of the Cowdray Club was opened on 22 June 1922 by Lady Cowdray who, upon the same day, also laid the foundation stone of the new headquarters of the College of Nursing. But the *British Journal of Nursing* found that it could not restrain itself from remarking: 'The subscription [to the Cowdray Club] is very reasonable. Richer women may be members by paying the double subscription, an economic arrangement which is not to our taste but apparently the nursing profession has now become inured to charity and patronage since the campaign for the Nation's Fund for Nurses was inaugurated by Lady Cowdray. Nurses who prefer to pay as they go can do so by joining the Royal British Nurses Association Club' . . . etc., etc.

CHAPTER TWELVE

The Voluntary System in Jeopardy

AN APPOINTMENTS BUREAU had been opened directly after the signing of the Armistice in 1918. This the College Council had found necessary because the powers-that-were started demobilizing nurses from the Forces at no more than twenty-four hours' notice. Such a thing strains belief today; nevertheless it was a fact. The College made a public protest and demanded that nurses being demobilized should be treated, anyway, with some of the limited privileges accorded to soldiers and sailors.

The College asked for a month's notice with allowances for nurses. Some peculiar individual in Whitehall who had not the slightest care what the general public might think, replied that nothing could be done because 'there was no such provision under which nurses had entered service'. There had been no such provision promising gratuities to fighting service ranks, but the Government just did not dare turn them out into civil life penniless. Still, there were many more of them which made a difference.

After considerable lobbying and campaigning, however, the College did get a grudging agreement that sisters should be given one week's notice and one week's pay and allowances on demobilization and that the week could be taken as leave. This was better than nothing. Meanwhile the Appointments Bureau was working overtime finding jobs for nurses, and succeeded in placing them not only in Britain but in various parts of the Empire, before the Bureau was finally closed, after matters had settled down in 1920.

At the same time the College was continuing a long campaign conducted against the naval authorities, who had given their nurses no rise in pay since the outbreak of war although the average hours worked were far more than in any other service.

There was, of course, some reason for the working-hours; unless a far greater complement of sick-bay staff was carried at sea than was possible under war conditions, long hours could not be avoided. In this the sailors, themselves, were literally in the same boat. There was, however, no excuse of the kind in the great naval hospitals ashore.

At first, all the College could get was an Admiralty assurance that 'The matter was under consideration' which they knew perfectly well would mean that nothing would happen unless the pressure was kept up. This was done and a year later a part-triumph achieved when the Admiralty agreed to pay gratuities to those demobilized after a given length of service, and also to 'review excessive hours of work'.

In 1920 College membership had risen to well over 17,000, immensely greater than that of any other nursing organization. Gertrude Cowlin's local centres were proliferating and had already advanced to granting local scholarships; there were also four residential clubs among them. But there were great and grave problems facing the profession which the College must try to solve if it was to retain its position as the leading nursing organization. The first concerned salaries. Nurses were still ill-paid and overworked. The war had made little difference to their conditions owing to the rising prices of everything needful. Living accommodation in many of the smaller hospitals was a disgrace. These matters must be put right—the question was, how?

Rising prices had hit the hospitals supported by voluntary contributions just as hard as everyone else; all hospitals other than asylums and infirmaries run out of taxpayers money by local authorities were 'voluntary'. The principle was one of the most prized in both the nursing and medical professions. It gave both the freedom from lay control by which their professions could more rightly be called devoted vocations. This had a very great deal to recommend it, but while some of the greater voluntary hospitals were rich, most of the smaller ones were poor.

It was necessary that nurses' pay must be raised and their hours lowered, but the question remained as to where the money necessary to these objects was to come from. Meanwhile the

College Council decided to print and publish its Register of Members in order that hospitals, others concerned, and the general public should have an immediate means of checking upon individual qualifications.

It was in 1920, also, that Gertrude Cowlin's magnificent work for the College received an even wider appreciation. She was elected Assistant Director of the League of Red Cross Societies at Geneva. In the years that followed this responsibility caused her to travel to most parts of the world but, until her retirement, she never ceased to work in any way possible for the College.

In the early 'twenties the work of the Appointments Bureau was done so it was re-formed as an Enquiry and Information Bureau dealing with all matters concerning nursing and public health. A legal advice service was also instituted by which Sir Charles Russell, one of the most famous lawyers of the era, gave his services on nursing problems to all College members, free. The Council in this year set up a Loan Fund for nurses who found themselves in temporary difficulties.

A subscription of five shillings 'to help pay the costs of the College of Nursing Bulletin' was launched simultaneously.

At the end of the first year of publication, since it proved expensive, members were asked if they wanted it to continue and if it contained the sort of material they wanted to read. The general average of reply was that members wanted it enlarged, with more clinical articles, but—having regard to the five shillings 'subscription to help pay costs'—still wanted it to be issued free.

This was done until 1926 when an agreement was made with Macmillan Ltd., publishers, that the *Nursing Times*, already published by that firm, should become the Official Journal of the College in place of the Bulletin. At that time editorial control was vested in the College which provided the leading article and appointed and paid the Editor. Subsequent agreements over the years have led to a change in the position, so that at the time of writing, while the *Nursing Times* is the journal for the Rcn, the Editor is appointed and paid by the publishers who have full editorial control, and the views expressed in the various articles, including the leading articles,

are those of the writers and do not necessarily reflect the policy
of the Rcn. A four-page College supplement is, however, now
included in the journal each month, giving College news
and views.

A hospital ward, from a photograph taken many years ago, at The Hospital for Sick Children, London

The opening of the Headquarters building, May 1926

Queen Mary leaves the building after the opening of the
College of Nursing

Photo: Walter N

Students of today—the Royal Free Hospital, London

CHAPTER THIRTEEN

Royal Occasions

THE COLLEGE OF NURSING headquarters building in Henrietta Place was opened by Queen Mary in a setting which had justifiably been made spectacular. On Monday, 21 May 1926, a Guard of Honour was ready in the entrance, its members being drawn from the nursing services of the Crown, the hospitals, and public health and domiciliary nurses from all parts of the country. A military band struck up the National Anthem as the Queen stepped out of her Daimler with her Lady-in-Waiting, the Dowager Countess of Airlie, and her Gentleman-in-Waiting, Mr. Harry Verney.

Ready to receive her were the Archbishop of Canterbury, Dame Sarah Swift, the College president, the Members of the College Council, and the Hon. Sir Arthur Stanley, the Chairman; Lady Cowdray, the Minister of Health, the Mayor of St. Marylebone, and Sir Edwin Cooper, F.R.I.B.A., the architect of the new structure. Fortunately the day was fine and there was a cheerful crowd packing Cavendish Square and Henrietta Place to roar its appreciation of the show. One of the great moments came as the Queen paused on entering the building to smile and chat with Princess Arthur of Connaught, who was among the invited guests. Every nurse there knew that Princess Arthur had taken regulation training and was entitled to the magic letters S.R.N.—and the cheers in the constricted area of the building were deafening.

Everything went perfectly. On the decorated platform at the end of the Memorial Hall, Lady Cowdray formally asked the Queen to accept the title-deeds of the building, and presented the documents. The Queen thereupon handed them to Dame Sarah Swift, saying: 'I have great pleasure in transferring to you the deed of gift of this beautiful building, which I now declare open.'

In a short speech Dame Sarah spoke what was in everybody's thoughts—the deep and genuine sense of gratitude everyone concerned with the College felt towards Lady Cowdray, who had not only presented the building but had provided all the furniture and equipment. 'For many years past Lady Cowdray has championed the cause of nurses,' said Dame Sarah in conclusion, 'and in doing so discovered that wider facilities for post-graduate teaching, practical and theoretical, were required, and thus decided to build the College. Since she laid the foundation stone four years ago she has never ceased in her efforts to make it what she felt it ought to be as the headquarters of the Nursing Profession.'

With that phrase, spoken in the presence of the first Lady in the Kingdom, the College of Nursing was finally and fully established as supreme in its field. In the first ten years of its life, despite ceaseless, cleverly organized opposition, it had come far as Sir Arthur Stanley pointed out in the main speech of the ceremony. The College membership had reached over 25,000, a figure larger by many times over than any other nursing organization in the country. He also referred to the Nation's Fund for Nurses, of which Lady Cowdray had been treasurer. The Tribute Fund had already reached over £100,000, and he gave an outline of the magnificent relief work it had already made possible. The Endowment Fund, although it had progressed more slowly, had reached over £68,000. Best of all, however, was the fact that these great sums had been raised by the work and devotion of nurses from those who had nursing interests at heart.

There was a moving moment when Sir Arthur announced that he had received a letter from Dame Sidney Browne, the first President of the College, who had been unable through illness to attend the ceremony. In the letter Dame Sidney enclosed a cheque for £300 to endow lectures on tropical diseases and the necessary nursing techniques. Finally, Sir Arthur emphasized that the College had striven and was striving to secure better conditions in hospitals and in private nursing. Further, it was actively engaged upon a scheme for pensions and superannuation drawn up in conjunction with the King Edward's Hospital Fund for London and other organizations. This had already been put before the hospital authorities, and it could be hoped that after negotiation it might be adopted.

These announcements, coming at the same time as the royal opening ceremony, received wide notice in the national as well as the nursing and medical Press. That they did not make acceptable reading to Mrs. Bedford Fenwick was, in the circumstances, only to be expected. There was no way round the three hard facts contained in the reports—the immensely greater membership of the College of Nursing than the R.B.N.A., the total of its Endowment Fund, and the fact that the Queen, no less, accepted it as the headquarters of the nursing profession.

It is a tribute to Ethel Bedford Fenwick's indomitable spirit that—possibly in foreknowledge of the Queen's decision to perform the opening ceremony—she struck again. For it was in that same year that she launched the rival British College of Nurses with an endowment (believed to be from one of her husband's wealthy patients) greater than that of the existing College.

The British College existed for a good many years but it never approached the College of Nursing in membership figures, and did not receive the constant interest and patronage which the latter received from Queen Mary. The Queen's instincts as a mother were as deep as her belief in the poise and dignity necessary to her position. She had lost a young son, Prince John, tragically. Her second son, Prince Bertie (afterwards King George VI), was delicate. Her interest in nursing was genuine and by no means assumed as merely part of her royal duties. It was later that same year that Queen Mary consented to become first Patron of the College of Nursing.

From the day of her opening of the College headquarters building she became a regular visitor. Her calls, in the normal way, were notified in advance from the palace, but there were occasions when her Daimler was at the door and her footman handing her down before anyone on the College staff had an idea that she was coming. The following wild scramble to find the most senior official present, and that lady's descent to the hallway frantically patting hair, became the joy of the juniors.

There was a suspicion that the Queen, who had a sense of humour, took a little wicked pleasure in it, too, but she never showed it by the slightest shade of expression.

The Cowdray Club kitchen of the period produced a cake of such quality that it had become famous among professional women in London. On one of her first informal calls the Queen tried a slice and pronounced almost poetically upon its excellence. At the next call, naturally, when tea was ordered-up from the kitchen a Cowdray Club cake was ordered too. But when the hostess of the afternoon offered it, her silver knife poised, the Queen stayed her.

'Oh, please don't cut it,' she asked. 'I described it to the King last week, and he is *most* anxious to try it. May I take it with me, do you think?'

At her next call the Queen brought the information that King George V had given unqualified approval to the cake, and would appreciate some more. Among those whose duties lay with Buckingham Palace there would have been no surprise at this. There was a genuine homely affection between the King and Queen; apart from the dignity which both felt should rigidly be upheld about the situation in life in which they found themselves, they thought about each other and took effort to please each other precisely as any other English couple who were fortunate in finding happiness together. The King, as is common knowledge, had a somewhat primitive (but never *risqué*) sense of humour. He also, like most born sailors, had a sweet tooth as the saying goes.

The Cowdray Club cake became his favourite. Therefore whenever the Queen dropped in to tea at the College—which she did from that day to the end of her life—a Cowdray cake was always on the table. But it was never cut. Before the Queen left, it had been unobtrusively slipped into a cardboard box and handed to the footman in the front seat of the waiting Daimler. No one ever referred to the matter and no one kept a count of the cakes the King got for tea by this time-honoured transaction.

Naturally, the Queen's informal visits were far from being the only ones she made to the College. The friendships she made among the staff, she valued. In general terms the College realized that it could rely upon the Queen to help—if her crowded appointments allowed—by appearing at any function of benefit to the profession. One such, the object of which is of no importance at this day, was memorable.

In the entrance hall, a few minutes before the Queen's car was due, a College reception party was drawn up, with notable guests, with the (then) Mayor of St. Marylebone, and of course with everybody in their best bibs and tuckers, complete with Orders and medals. After which it seemed that some freakish spirit of misrule took over command.

At the first sign of activity a minion, recognized as being on the Cowdray Club staff, bustled out on to the red carpet which reached to the kerbstone and proceeded to brush and comb the fringed edges—with an ordinary, domestic comb and hairbrush. Nobody in the reception party liked to move; most were so astounded by the apparition that they couldn't do so. The minion was whispered at, hissed at, finally as the blue Daimler was seen in Cavendish Square, she was directly shouted at.

It was a windy day. She heard at last, glanced round to see the contorted faces of the gorgeously attired reception party, and fled, terrified, to the oblivion from whence she came.

At which moment the gusting wind picked up a heap of dry refuse nicely arranged by a departed roadman and showered it in defilement across the sacred purity of the scarlet carpet.

Hearts stood still—but not the stout heart of the College caretaker, a war veteran in his best turn-out a-clink with medals. The caretaker plunged for an inner recess, grabbed a broom, and dashed out of the entrance. Swinging heroically, he sent the dust and leaves flying with the broom. The carpet was clear—almost—as the royal Daimler slid beside it, stopping to the correct inch. As the footman alighted, hat in hand, to open the door for the Queen the wind spiralled a cloud of dust raised by the caretaker's broom.

Before the royal foot had touched the carpet, however, the caretaker had turned and run back to efface himself and his broom. With his eyes full of dust he plunged through the entrance and met the Mayor coming out with such violence that each had to cling to the other to preserve balance. But, on trying to break away from each other, they found themselves joined by the caretaker's medals which had become tangled with the Mayor's chain of office. It was a tangle which both sought to unravel in gasping hurry, and only made worse. As the Queen reached the doorway the broom escaped the caretaker's clutch and fell with a crash. . . .

If the Queen saw the spectacle she gave no sign. Her expression, as usual, was one of smiling, benign dignity. But there were those who noticed that one of her hands was pressed to her side, and that more than a suspicion of tears stood in her eyes. . . .

CHAPTER FOURTEEN

Royal Charter—the Background

THE EFFECT of the war by which people able to pay for nursing attention had lost their fear of hospitals, brought two new factors in its train. Such people could pay for private cubicles or rooms in most of the big hospitals, and thus avoid the public wards. The quality of treatment they received was no different from that of the ward patients, except that they could if they wished also pay for the attention of whatever specialist or consultant they favoured. The great advantage was, of course, privacy, and there was also human snobbery in being able to receive visitors apart from the common herd, and thus demonstrating the possession of means.

This was a thoroughly good system, it has worked well from those days to these, it is of financial benefit to the organization and if it panders to the smaller human weaknesses there is no great harm in that.

The second factor was the sudden and spectacular rise in the number of private nursing homes and convalescent homes—a total which doubled in the decade of the 'twenties. None of these homes could provide the quality of treatment given by the voluntary hospitals. Not even the best of them could match normal hospital equipment. Some of the worst became, by the blind vagary of fashion, the 'smartest' to be ill in, and charged outrageous prices. There was usually a certificated sister or so on the staff, but the nurses were for the greater part untrained and chosen more for their appearance and social manners than anything else.

There is no doubt that there were doctors who had a share in such homes and recommended wealthy patients. A vivid and factual picture of one such fashionable nursing home is given by Dr. Cronin in his magnificent book *The Citadel*—which, incidentally, caused a considerable flurry in the upper echelons of the medical profession when it was published.

It is only fair to add that not all private nursing homes were run on such lines. A considerable number were started by fully trained nurses who could find the necessary capital; they charged reasonable prices and employed trained staff as far as they could afford. They were kept as clean and sterile as possible, unlike the example in Dr. Cronin's story. They fulfilled a need for those of the middle classes who still regarded entry into hospital, even in a pay-bed, as constituting a loss of status and prestige.

But practically none of these homes were especially designed and built for the purpose except some rare examples in the largest cities. Almost all of them functioned in middle-sized to large Victorian private houses, inconveniently designed traps for dust, which called for backbreaking work from the nurses . . . with the result that trained nurses would only work in them for a higher wage-rate than normal . . . which cut down the number of trained staff the homes could afford to employ.

The situation was that the best of the nursing homes could not provide hospital standard of treatment and attention, and the worst of them were a public scandal. The College, in attacking the problem over a period of years made itself unpopular with those doctors who, for various reasons, wanted no change.

By 1924 the College decided that the time had come to take action and the Parliamentary Committee drafted the Nursing Homes (Registration) Bill. This Bill was discussed at a conference at the Annual Meeting that year and presented to Parliament in February 1925. In June the College agreed to withdraw its Bill on receiving an assurance from the Government that it proposed to set up a select committee to inquire into the subject. This Select Committee was appointed in 1926 and a statement setting out the reasons for Registration and Inspection of Nursing Homes was submitted by the College, and many of these recommendations were included in the Committee's report which was published the following year. A redrafted Bill was presented and passed into law as the Nursing Homes (Registration) Act, 1927.

Not all the College demands were met by the measure, but with the principle of inspection and control accepted the

Council rightly felt that a considerable step forward had been made and arranged courses of instruction to help those who would have to carry out inspections under the Act.

At the Annual Meeting of the College in June 1926, the first to be held in the new headquarters, the proposal, 'That to further establish the position of the College, application be made for a Royal Charter', was carried unanimously. The proposal was considered and agreed by the Council and in December of that year at an Extraordinary General Meeting it was resolved that the College should petition His Majesty's Privy Council for incorporation by Royal Charter. The following year a draft Charter and Petition were submitted, the Petition, according to ancient form, being addressed to, 'The King's Most Excellent Majesty in Council'. The Petition set out the aims and objects of the College, its financial position, and its achievements to date.

An immediate objection was lodged with the Privy Council by Ethel Bedford Fenwick's Royal British Nurses Association, her British College of Nurses, and certain other bodies. One point made was that since the R.B.N.A., had already been granted a Royal Charter, there was surely no point in granting another to a second body claiming to represent the same profession.

There was, however, a point of overwhelming strength in favour of the grant; in outline it was the point that the College of Nursing not only had a vastly greater membership than any other nursing body but had done more for the profession than all the other bodies put together. Taken in full detail this point explains why the objections raised were to prove ineffective.

Within the first two years of its foundation the College had published what became known as the Nurses' Charter. This was the report and recommendations of a committee set up by the College in 1918 to examine salaries and conditions of service throughout the profession. A detailed questionnaire had been sent out by the Committee which was able to base its recommendations on the first-hand evidence of the answers received. The 'Nurses' Charter' was published and circulated to all nurse-employing authorities in 1919 with the request

7

that the improvements in salary scales and working conditions recommended should be adopted.

A number of hospitals and local authorities did so, but of course there were those which would make no concession unless by the demand of law. The College pursued its battle against them down the years to the institution of the National Health Service—and since then in discussions with the Management side on the Whitley Council.

In 1922 the College called a conference to discuss the conditions of non-resident nurses which, owing to the poor salaries offered, were in many cases outrageous. Under the Nurses' Charter the College had recommended salary scales for all grades which, in the money-value of the period, were no more than fair. The College therefore sent letters of protest to all authorities who advertised posts at less than these scales, and also made determined efforts to persuade the nursing and allied Press to refuse such advertisements. This was at first unsuccessful, but when *The Nursing Times** became the official journal of the College, it agreed not to accept advertisements which did not conform to the College recommendations.

In that same year the College had one of its great early triumphs by gaining an amendment to the Unemployment Insurance Amendment Bill which became an Act in 1922. By this amendment nurses, an underpaid and overworked body of women, were excluded from the Act, and were therefore not forced to contribute to a fund from which owing to the shortage of nurses they were never likely to benefit.

Steps taken by the College to gain this concession had started in 1920 when the Hours of Employment Bill and Unemployment Insurance Amendment Bill came before Parliament. The Council decided to seek the views of the membership through a referendum of members. The result showed that rules regarding hours of work and overtime pay were unthinkable in application to a profession dedicated to service; it must be left to nurses to decide what was best for the care and safety of patients. On this matter the College did not condone long hours, but made the important statement of principle that all negotiations with regard to conditions of work on

* See p. 77.

behalf of nurses should be made by nurses, and nothing should be imposed upon the profession by unqualified outside authority.

At this stage the Minister of Labour would not agree that nurses should be excluded from the Unemployment Amendment Bill partly because they had been arbitrarily included under the Act of 1918 and partly due to the low number of replies to the referendum of the College on this matter. The College therefore sent out a second referendum in 1921, and in the Bulletin* the membership was soundly berated for its slack reply to the first, which had been less than a quarter of its number; this, of course, had weakened the position of the College Council in discussions. The effect was immediate. No less than 35,000 signatures were received to a form of protest to the inclusion of nurses in the Unemployment Insurance scheme. This was presented to the Minister of Labour by a College deputation which pointed out that, owing to the shortage of nurses, no benefit could accrue to nurses forced to pay the contribution. There was, as there usually is, some final manoeuvring on the official side, but at last the College won its point. Incidentally, the nurses of the local centres had a considerable effect on the exclusion of nurses from the Act by systematically lobbying their respective M.P.s.

The great strength of the College through the years has been the opportunities it provided from the outset for members to express their views through the development of local centres and specialist sections.

The local centres, later to be called branches, provided a forum at which members could discuss general professional matters while the sections advised on specialist problems. The College Council therefore had the means of obtaining at any time the views of the whole membership, and thus could rely upon a body of informed opinion at its back in whatever action it took over the years to improve the nursing service and nursing education, the conditions of nurses, and the training of students.

In the early days the local centres not only provided a meeting-place for members at which professional matters

* See pp. 68–77.

could be considered but were also concerned with educational activities, arranging post-certificate lectures, courses, and study days.

With the help and advice of Gertrude Cowlin quite extensive programmes were arranged. Through the Local Centres Standing Committee, later the Branches Standing Committee, to which each branch was entitled to send a representative, the views of the membership on current problems were made known and resolutions calling for action were considered and submitted to the Council.

Aware of the advantage which expert advice readily available from within the membership would provide, the Council in 1921 set up a Public Health Advisory Committee to advise upon the status and training of public health nurses, at that period a comparatively new branch of the profession dealing with preventive work This led to the institution of the Public Health Section of the College early in 1923. Meanwhile a conference of sister tutors in 1922 agreed that there should be opportunity for them to meet and confer together and that a body of expert opinion on this particular new branch of work could be of great value to the Council. The Sister Tutor Section of the College was therefore set up towards the end of the year; one of its first tasks was to consider a suitable syllabus of training for sister tutors.

As the sections developed, local groups were formed within the branches thus providing a meeting ground for members within the same field of work to discuss their common problems. The sections also produced a variety of reports and memoranda, some for submission to Government Departments, others of which were published, and organized conferences and study days on matters of concern to section members.

In Scotland the Board was expanding its work of bringing the College to the members, encouraging the establishment of local centres and the organization of post-certificate lectures and study days. It made representations to the Scottish Departments on matters affecting the profession, in particular, in the early days, on the rules and regulations of the General Nursing Council for Scotland on the registration of 'existing nurses', and later to the Council itself with regard to the training of student nurses. The first Annual General Meeting of the College to be held outside London was organized in Edinburgh in 1921 by the Scottish Board and the Edinburgh Centre when a most stimulating and interesting programme of professional and social events was arranged. The Board set up its own Public Health Advisory Committee to advise it on matters concerning all aspects of public health and later both Public Health and Sister Tutor Sections were established locally.

The Irish Board, owing to the troubled times, had to face many difficult problems in its early years and eventually was dissolved in 1925. The Belfast Centre, however, which had been enthusiastically active from the first, remained in being and became the focus of College activities in Northern Ireland.

In the first year of the College's existence education had been recognized as being one of the major objects of the organization's work. In 1917, therefore, a Consultative Committee was appointed to consider curricula for training schools and to consult with the schools about training standards. Between 1919 and 1920 there was consultation between the College and King's College for Women regarding the Sister Tutor Course which had been started by the latter in 1918. Provision was made for studies to be supervised by a suitably qualified nurse. It was at this time that the first reference to a proposed university degree for nurses was made, and a fund for the establishment of a Chair of Nursing was opened.

In the following year, 1921, the first university course for nurses was started in Leeds which established a Diploma in Nursing. Post-graduate courses on public health nursing were organized during the winter, and the College made representations to the Ministry of Health about the training and qualification of health visitors which were destined to bear fruit a few years later.

In 1924 the College was invited to co-operate with Bedford College and the League of Red Cross Societies in a course which had been started in 1922 for hospital administrators and instructors in schools of nursing. In this the College became responsible for the lectures on hospital administration, training-school administration, methods of teaching, and the history of nursing. This became known as the International Course because nurses from countries overseas attended, and it was the first, full-time, formal educational activity in the College history. It was in this year, significantly, that Gertrude Cowlin was appointed first Education Officer, a post which she combined with Librarian (in addition to other duties).

The result of the College's representations concerning health visitors in 1921 came in 1925 when the Ministry of Health invited College comments on a memorandum on health-visitor training. This was considered by the Public Health Section, and the Council embodied its findings in a draft scheme which was submitted to the Ministry, one of the most important recommendations being that the basic qualification for a health visitor should be three years general hospital training. At the same time the Council stated its intention of submitting a scheme by which the College should become a recognized training centre to qualify nurses for health visiting. Further the Council announced that it was not in favour of a Register of Health Visitors who should, in any case, be on the Register of the General Nursing Council. The outcome was that the College was approved by the Ministry of Health as a training centre; thereafter the first full-time course for health visitors' training was started, together with an evening course for existing health visitors who were eligible to sit for the examination.

The Student Nurses Association of the College was established in that same year, 1925, to bring students into touch with the professional organization which could afford them support and protection during their years of training. The Association was set up with its own organizing secretary, and units were very soon established in training schools throughout the country. Later, the Student Nurses Association became an entirely separate body although keeping its direct link with the College.*

In 1926 the University of London decided to grant a Diploma in Nursing. The College was represented on the Advisory Board and undertook the arrangement of lectures for nurses who wished to take the Diploma. By this time firmly established and recognized as the centre for post-certificate nurse education, the College arranged further lectures and courses for foreign

* See p. 172.

nurses, and in conjunction with the (then) Colonial Office, for nurses from all parts of the (then) British Empire.

The move of the headquarters staff into the new building presented by Lady Cowdray very greatly extended the educational facilities. In 1927 therefore the Council decided that a full-time Education Officer should be appointed. Again by the generosity of Lady Cowdray this was made possible, and Miss Ruth Hallowes, M.A. (Oxon.), S.R.N., was appointed. Miss Hallowes, who had trained at St. Thomas's Hospital, was later in the year granted a Rockefeller Foundation Travelling Scholarship to study nursing education and organization in America and Canada.

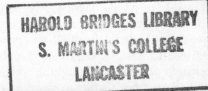

CHAPTER FIFTEEN

The Granting of the Charter

WITH all these achievements, a membership of over 26,000, and with the support of many training schools and a number of nursing and other organizations, the Petition of the College for the Grant of a Royal Charter was officially heard by a Committee of the Privy Council formed of Lord Warrington of Clyffe, Sir Maurice de Bunsen, and the Lord Advocate, Sir William Watson, on Wednesday, 29 February 1928. Mitchell Banks, K.C., and Cyril Asquith appeared for the College and Gavin Simmonds, K.C., and Howard Wright for the opposing bodies.

Mr. Banks, in his peroration, referred to all the points set forth in the Petition: the size of the College membership, the great educational work instituted by the College, and its professional and welfare activities on behalf of nurses.

In opposing the Petition, Gavin Simmonds, K.C., made the best possible of an embarrassingly empty brief, but he could do no more than urge his clients' view that the College's achievements had not justified the granting of a Charter. To this Mitchell Banks, K.C., made the obvious but none the less shattering reply that he thought it 'unfortunate' that his learned friend had not been able to state anything achieved for the nursing profession by the opposing bodies.

The result was that Lord Warrington, after conferring with his colleagues, announced that the Committee would report in favour of the College. Later the Council received formal notification 'That on 13th June 1928 His Majesty in Council was pleased to approve the grant of a Charter to the College of Nursing.'

There followed the necessary formalities of authorization by the members for the Council to accept the Charter as approved by the Privy Council and the winding up of the College of Nursing as a Limited Company.

The Charter 'as settled by His Majesty's Privy Council' was approved by the members at the Annual Meeting in June 1928 and on 28 July of that year the Charter was formally granted 'by warrant under the King's sign manual'.

The grant of the title 'Royal' does not automatically follow with the grant of a Royal Charter, but has to be applied for and good and sufficient reasons given for the honour to be accorded. This application was made in due course some eleven years later, and granted by the reigning Monarch.

Her Majesty Queen Mary who had become Patron of the College of Nursing Limited in 1926 continued as Patron of the College when it was incorporated by Royal Charter.

The following year—1929—the Bye-Laws which the Council had been authorized to draw up were presented to the Annual Meeting and adopted. The approval of the Privy Council was granted in December.

During the 1930s the Council and the Sections were continuously concerned with matters affecting the status of the profession and the service it gave to the community. Recommendations were made to Government Departments and the Statutory bodies regarding the training of students, the supply of suitable candidates, qualifications and training for different fields of work, interchangeability of pensions, an extention of the home nursing service, conditions of work for private nurses and standards in private nursing homes. A Private Nurses Committee was set up in 1930 which drew up a schedule of recommended salaries and conditions for private nurses which was circulated to all private nursing co-operations with the recommendation that these should be adopted. Subsequently with a view to protecting both the private nurse and the public from exploitation the Council agreed to a proposal from the Committee that the College should establish a Roll of Private Nursing Co-operations whose standards were approved by the College. Finally a Private Nurses Section was set up in 1938.

Meanwhile the desirability of strengthening the College in the areas had been under discussion. A special committee appointed by the Council to look into the matter drew up a draft scheme of Area Organization which proposed that in view of the development of the work a certain amount of administration should be carried out in areas and that whole-time area organizers should be appointed. The Council approved the scheme and referred it to the branches for con-sideration. The scheme was generally welcomed and its establishment formally approved by the Council in 1932, four area organizers being appointed to cover the Northern, Midland, Eastern, and Western areas of England and Wales, and one for Scotland. At the same time consideration had been given to the constitution of the branches and membership of branches and sections. It will be remembered that in 1920 an annual subscription of five shillings for new members of the College had been introduced; members wishing to belong to a branch or section had to pay a small additional fee direct to the branch or section. It was realized that in order to meet the additional cost of the Area Organization Scheme the annual subscription would have to be raised, and the suggestion was put forward that in future the subscription should be an inclusive one to include membership of a branch or section. This proposal was accepted and the subscription raised to £1 from which capitation fees were paid to branches and sections from headquarters.

In 1937 the twenty-first anniversary of the founding of the College was marked by the gift of a Presidential Badge of Office by the Leicester Branch and a Chain to the Badge by the Manchester and East Lancashire Branch.

It was in this year of its majority that the whole College was saddened by the death of its 'Foundress', Dame Sarah Swift, 'to whose vision and foresight' the Council, in paying tribute to her, recorded in its Minutes, 'must be accorded the inception of the College which from its foundation in 1916, she loved and served unceasingly'.

It would undoubtedly have been for Dame Sarah the culmination of a dream had she been alive in 1939 when it was announced that His Majesty King George VI had been 'graciously pleased to command that the College shall be known as "The Royal College of Nursing".' The title 'Royal' is not granted lightly. It reflects the achievements of the College and justifies the faith of its founders that it was granted this dis-

tinction so comparatively early in its life. A letter from Queen
Mary's Lady-in-Waiting expressed Her Majesty's pleasure in
the words: 'The new title emphasizes the standing the College
has long had, not only in this country but all over the world,
and as its Patron the Queen rejoices in the recognition which
the King has bestowed on an organization of such national and
international significance'. At the Annual General Meeting the
following year the necessary amendment to the Royal Charter
to incorporate the new title was carried unanimously, the
formalities being completed by the assent of 'His Majesty in
Council' to the amendment.

In 1946 a grant of arms was accorded to the College by the
College of Arms. Emblazoned on a blue shield are the sun and
stars, denoting the day and night service which nurses give;
the shield is surmounted by the open book of learning and a
Roman lamp which has been authorized by the College of
Arms as the heraldic symbol of nursing. Inscribed at the base
of the shield is the motto *Tradimus Lampada*—'We hand on the
Torch'. The Royal College of Nursing was the first women's
organization to be granted the right by the College of Arms to
emblazon its arms on a shield rather than a lozenge in recognition of nurses' active service in war.

CHAPTER SIXTEEN

Educational Development

THE KEYNOTE of the College policy in education from the earliest days has been its insistence upon professional influence and control over the professional content of courses of training. It is no paradox that in achieving this the Council has always made the fullest use of non-nursing experts as lecturers in specialized subjects and sought the advice of specialists from the field of general education.

In the years that followed the granting of the Royal Charter and up to the outbreak of war in 1939 the College was constantly in touch with King's College of Household and Social Science, previously King's College for Women, making recommendations concerning the syllabus for the Sister Tutor Course, with Bedford College regarding the International Course in Hospital Administration, and with the University of London regarding the Diploma in Nursing. As the technical aspect of care of the sick became progressively more complex over the years the College aimed at more comprehensive and better preparation of nurses for the senior posts in order to provide a higher standard of training for the student, and an efficient nursing service. In addition to the foregoing, study weeks and refresher courses were constantly arranged for the different branches of nursing, and the attendance increased yearly.

As a result of the increasing development of educational work, the College established a separate Educational Department and in 1930 Miss H. C. Parsons, O.B.E. was appointed Director. Miss Parsons who had been a V.A.D. during the First World War, entered the Nightingale Training School at St. Thomas's Hospital in 1919, gaining an Honour Certificate on passing her hospital examinations and winning the Gold Medal for her year. Subsequently she qualified in midwifery, became Sister in various surgical and medical wards at St. Thomas's, then Night Superintendent and later Second Assistant Matron. During this time she also prepared students for the state examinations and, in 1929, obtained the Diploma in Nursing of the University of London.

It was during Miss Parsons's Directorate that the Midwife Teachers Course was established in 1930 at the College at the request of the Central Midwives Board. Special consideration in conjunction with the Public Health Section became necessary during this period concerning the basic training required for health visitors, and representations were made to the General Nursing Council for a more comprehensive course of training for student nurses. Later, a special committee was set up by the Education Committee on which representatives of the sections served, to consider widening the scope of the general basic training of students.

A practical scheme of training was drawn up with a view to meeting the criticisms which were frequently made regarding the limitations of the existing syllabus of training for nurses. The College recommended to the General Nursing Council that this should be implemented and that the Preliminary State Examination should be divided into two parts, one of which might be taken before entering hospital. Only the latter, however, was finally accepted and put into operation.

Of special interest today is an investigation which the College then carried out into the possibility of establishing Schools of Nursing on sounder educational lines in which the nurses in training should be students of the school and not employed directly as staff of the hospital. At that time the obvious financial difficulties involved in such a scheme formed a barrier, but the same recommendations were later to be made by the Committee under Lord Horder* and in the latest (1964) report on nursing education issued by the Committee under Sir Harry Platt.†

An example of how the College always strove to meet the needs of the profession and of the community at large is illustrated by its inception of the Industrial Nursing Course in 1934. An increasing number of health centres were being

* See p. 116.   † See p. 178.

established within industry which, of course, led to a demand for nurses to staff them. The Industrial Nursing Course for the College Certificate was originally one year full-time, or six months part-time for those already engaged in the work.

In 1939, under the immediate threat of war, the College organized practical nursing courses in hospitals throughout the country for trained nurses who were joining the new Civil Nursing Reserve.

During her years as Director of the Education Department Miss Parsons saw the educational work of the College develop out of all recognition. It was through her determination and energy that the Department was built up and established as a national and international centre for post-certificate nursing education. She represented the College on the most important committees and bodies dealing with the professional education of nurses; she strove especially through the universities and other bodies to ensure that nurse education should take its rightful place in all other schemes of adult education.

On the outbreak of war in September 1939 the International Course at Bedford College had to be closed down and King's College for Household and Social Science where the Sister Tutor Course was held, was evacuated to Leicester. A stepping stone in the history of the Education Department, was the establishment of a Tutor Course at the College itself. This course for which a Royal College Certificate was granted was known as the 'Nurse Teachers' Course', because provision was made within its syllabus for teachers in other post-certificate work as well as for tutors in nurse-training schools.

There was, of course, a pressing demand for intensive nurse training after war broke out. This especially applied to industrial nursing; the Government realized the man-hours that could be saved in factories by skilled, on-the-spot care of workers' health. Accordingly the Ministry of Labour arranged with the College for specialized one-month training courses in industrial nursing, and the Government paid the expenses of nurses attending them. The six-months' course for the Royal College Certificate was still continued, and an Industrial Nursing Advisory Committee was set up to deal with the problems that arose.

Correspondence courses for nurses already working in industry were started together with lectures for nurses working in shelters and rest-centres; it was College policy to ensure that these wherever possible should be manned by trained health visitors. Lectures in first aid and home nursing were also started for Nursing Auxiliaries under the auspices of the St. John's Ambulance Brigade.

Special courses for nurses employed in war-time nurseries were started in 1941, and a scheme for a nine-months' course for qualification as health visitor and district nurse was approved by the Ministry of Health and began in 1943. By then the College was already looking ahead to conditions likely to follow the end of the war; it foresaw the demand for qualified nurse-dietitions, and instituted an eighteen-months' dietetic course. In that same year the College was represented by Miss Parsons and other nurses on a Colonial Office Committee to study the training necessary for nurses serving in the Colonies. An Educational Advisory Board composed of leading nursing, medical, and general educationalists was also set up by the College to advise on future policy and the promotion of post-certificate nursing education.

The war had brought increasing demands upon the library which was badly in need of room for expansion. The necessary accommodation was made possible by a grant in 1943 of £1,000 from the Halford Bequest; the first full-time Librarian (a nurse) was appointed and two years later the new Library of the College was opened by Princess Elizabeth now Her Majesty the Queen.

A one-year, full-time Nursing Administration Course was instituted in 1944 for potential matrons. It was hoped that this would become recognized by employing authorities as the appropriate qualification for those applying for matron posts. In the following year, the last of the war, the Educational Advisory Board prepared a memorandum which was forwarded to the Ministry of Education recommending that grants should be provided for nursing education; a request was added that the Ministry should receive a deputation from the College to discuss the proposals. In view of the delay in acceding to this request, it was decided to leave the matter in abeyance until the report of the Working Party on the Recruitment and Training of Nurses* should be published. Meanwhile, on the advice of the Board the College decided that as from 1946 entrants for the Tutor Course should prepare for the University of London Sister Tutor Diploma, and the College course was reorganized to meet the University requirements.

With the end of the war in 1945 arrangements for courses of study for overseas nurses were resumed and the number of refresher courses much extended. Students were also received from Commonwealth Territories and special arrangements made for World Health Organization scholars.

In 1948 Mary F. Carpenter, who had joined the staff as Assistant to the Director in the Education Department in 1943, was appointed Director on the retirement of Miss Parsons.

Trained at the Nightingale School at St. Thomas's Hospital, Mary Carpenter took her Midwifery Certificate at Norwich City Maternity Home, was successful in the Sister Tutor Course at the College and obtained the Diploma in Nursing at the University of London. She was successively Night Assistant, Ward Sister, and Sister Tutor at St. Thomas's and in the early part of the war served in London and sector hospitals. She was appointed, as Miss Parsons had been before her, to serve on a number of bodies concerned with nursing education.

In the years that immediately followed her appointment, Mary Carpenter studied nursing education and administration on a Rockefeller Travelling Fellowship in America and Canada. International recognition of the College as an important centre of post-certificate nursing education is shown in the invitations to her by the World Health Organization and other international bodies to advise on nursing education. The educational work of the College also received special acknowledgement in 1932 when the Ministry of Education recognized it officially as a major establishment for further education. A major step forward in expanding the College facilities for post-certificate education outside the London area was achieved by the opening of the Birmingham Centre in 1953.

* See p. 141.

As the years go by the College is continually prepared to respond to changing needs for preparatory and refresher courses and to vary methods as the situation demands. New positions have been created to deal with new needs, and so new courses have been established to prepare for posts such as teachers of pupil nurses, clinical instructors, and field-work instructors in public-health nursing.

CHAPTER SEVENTEEN

The Lancet *Commission*

DURING THE 'twenties, and for long afterwards, the suggestion of 'Nationalizing the Hospitals' raised horror among most trained nurses (and doctors) who regarded the voluntary contributions on which hospitals were supported as something akin to the money which people willed to convents or other religious bodies.

The thing was part of a high instinct in human nature. People gave of their substance so that those of vocation and training could allay some of the world's misery and suffering.

This feeling was very real and widespread. It was well known that specialists gave their services free to the poor in the larger hospitals. Further, among general practitioners there were very many who sent small bills or no bills to their poorer patients, but made up the scale when accounting to those better off. Moreover, thousands of men in all walks of civilian life had seen the inside of hospitals in wartime and realized that they were no longer antechambers to the mortuary. They were impressed by the skill of the doctors and the cleanliness and care of the nurses. They soon understood that surgery was not for private houses but could only be safe and effective in properly equipped and sterilized hospital theatres.

The voluntary system of hospital support was generally held to be a good system, a practical form of idealism which got the best out of all in its ranks. But it was rapidly becoming clear that as a system it could not pay its way.

Nursing had always been an under-paid and over-disciplined profession, but after the great emancipation of women brought about by the war, nurses were beginning to show restiveness. This was not surprising since comparison of their working hours and pay with those of women in commercial offices showed an entirely unjust and unfair difference.

The first year of any nurse's service in hospital was mostly spent in cleaning, scrubbing, and dealing with bed-pans. Probationers in the 'thirties were paid £20 first year, £25 second year and £30 third year, on average, and staff nurses received up to £60. Of course all on the staff received board and lodging.

Naturally, only girls and women who were dedicated to nursing would endure conditions which were exacerbated by a tradition of constant bullying and purposeful fault-finding by the sisters. This had its parallel in the ranks of the Regular Army, and it was upon Army traditions and customs that Florence Nightingale had founded skilled nursing. The Army believed that discipline could only be maintained if commissioned officers were kept within a high Brahmin caste, and if the non-commissioned officers ruled by terrorism. Once a private soldier got his first stripe, therefore, he was required to bully and roar. And generally liked it, since human creatures vary little in essentials.

Precisely the same thing happened with the average nurse on promotion, not because of anything wrong about the dedicated nurse-character but because the hospital tradition of the time (and for long afterwards) demanded it. The probationer of the 'thirties, therefore, was constantly harassed and driven. There were humiliating punishments for minor omissions. No nurse spoke to a sister, matron, or doctor without first being addressed unless in a case of emergency. Doctors were creatures of glory from whom the dutiful nurse always averted her eyes.

It was inevitable that the young nurses of the period should begin to realize that they were of somewhat more use to the community than girls who sat anointing their finger-nails behind reception desks, but who were receiving eight or nine times their rate of pay.

On the Council of the College of Nursing there were disciplinarians who were also women of first-class mentality and long experience. They realized that the world was altering, especially as it affected their own sex. As a result the College was first among the nursing organizations to bring influence to bear against the most senseless of the disciplinary rules of the period.

The Council knew well that, quite apart from salary-rates, the general conditions in which a vast number of nurses were working were far short of being good and further from being ideal. For a considerable time an effort had been made to collect evidence and prepare a general case with all the detail necessary for any demand for reform. This was not an easy task; all evidence needed careful checking.

The Council, therefore, was both relieved and pleased when the proprietors of the famous medical journal *The Lancet* undertook the burden and, in December 1930, appointed a Commission 'To enquire into the reasons for the shortage of candidates trained and untrained for nursing the sick in general and special hospitals throughout the country, and to offer suggestions for making the service more attractive to women suitable for this necessary work'.

The Lancet Commission found—with good reason—that 'the nurse's conditions of training and service have fallen into relative disfavour not only with young people in search of a career but also with their advisers and with women in other professions'. But it reported that 'the standards of the profession could not be maintained merely by an economic appeal'. It was in favour of higher salaries for nurses but not for student nurses. One of its recommendations which is especially interesting was that girls should be allowed to take part of the Preliminary State Examination (anatomy, physiology, and hygiene) while still at school. This would obviously reduce the commitment of the nurse-training schools. The General Nursing Council would not agree to this since they were not empowered to allow any not directly appointed by them to conduct their examinations. However the suggestion was agreed to in later years.*

The main recommendations of the Commission 'to restore the popularity of nursing among educated girls' had little chance of widespread adoption at the period since the most important item—salaries—could not be dictated by anyone. The municipal hospitals were already paying more than most of the voluntary for the good reason that their finances were obtained by taxation. It was becoming grimly plain that the

* Nurses' (Amendment No.2) Rules, Approval Instrument 1953.

voluntary hospitals must have exchequer help in some way, but if they accepted it their independence would be lost.

The College had repeatedly been asking the Minister of Health for an official inquiry into nursing conditions. The Council's earnest recommendations to hospital managements to agree modest salary-rises and a reduction in working hours had met with little response. But sections of the younger members of other organizations had been taking matters into their own hands.

The Guild of Nurses (Nursing Section of the National Union of County Officers) had organized spectacular sandwich-board parades of nurses, wearing masks over their faces, to demand amendment of pay and hours. Much was made of the face-masks 'to avoid victimization' which was swallowed whole by a large number of popular-newspaper readers. Fenner Brockway, a clever and sincere Labour leader, presented a Bill to Parliament 'to lay down minimum wages and maximum hours for the nursing profession'.

His wage-rates were high, but he did not advocate hospital nationalization, so where the money was to come from was left vague. His maximum hours at 44 compared reasonably with the College's existing demand for a weekly 48. His Bill came to nothing, in fact, but it received immense publicity.

Finally in November 1937 an Interdepartmental Committee on Nursing Services was set up by the Minister of Health in conjunction with the Board of Education under the chairmanship of the Earl of Athlone. Its terms of reference were: 'To enquire into the arrangements at present in operation with regard to the recruitment, training, registration, and terms and conditions of service of persons engaged in nursing the sick, and to report whether any changes in those arrangements or any other measures are expedient for the purpose of maintaining an adequate service both for institutional and domiciliary nursing.'

CHAPTER EIGHTEEN

The Athlone Committee

THIS INTER-DEPARTMENTAL COMMITTEE ON NURSING SERVICES was the first official inquiry into the care of the sick, on a national scale, that had ever been made. The Committee opened its proceedings by sending out a questionnaire which was answered in detail by well over two thousand hospitals covering all parts of the United Kingdom and Northern Ireland. The greater problems of the nursing service were expressed in two of the facts brought out by the answers.

In the voluntary hospitals only 18 per cent of the ward staffs, including sisters, were fully trained, while the figure for all hospitals was only 31 per cent.

Hours worked by probationers in voluntary hospitals were up to 140 per fortnight on night duty and 108-111 on day duty. Local authority hospital figures were similar but night duty was lower at an average of 119.

Salary rates were little different from those already quoted for the 'thirties. The shortage of trained nurses was worse than it had been seven years before when *The Lancet* Commission published its findings.

Since the College had repeatedly asked for a Government inquiry it was especially keen to ensure that the Athlone Committee should have a comprehensive guide as to what was really necessary to put the nursing service on a sound footing. A memorandum of evidence, which is probably the most exhaustive ever produced covering the profession as a whole, was prepared by the College and submitted to the Committee early in 1938. (It was subsequently printed and published.)

In the first place the memorandum suggested that the only way to view the situation was from the attitude of supply and demand; apart from other forms of nursing, how many hospital beds were there? What proportion of beds to qualified nurses was necessary for efficiency? What was the increase in demand in the immediate past—and what, therefore, was it likely to be in the future? To all of which the memorandum had carefully worked-out answers for the Committee to test against their own findings.

The memorandum went on to list recommended salary scales and to insist that rises were necessary in all grades if future recruiting was to succeed, and pressed—as the College had pressed continually since its inception—for managements to institute a superannuation scheme on a national scale. Some schemes were already in being but they varied widely and were not interchangeable; in many instances no pension scheme was provided.

In offering these facts the memorandum explained that the College had every means of knowing all details since it now had a membership of just on 30,000 qualified nurses, a separate Board in Scotland, 108 branches and sub-branches in the United Kingdom, a Sister Tutor Section, a Public Health Section, a Private Nurses Advisory Committee, and a Student Nurses Association over 6,000 strong.

Backed by a mass of figures and statistics the memorandum called for measures that would encourage qualified nurses to study for further post-certificate qualifications, and for an overhaul of the system which would offer them a much wider chance of promotion. It suggested pre-nursing courses between school and hospital for student nurses, and a greater latitude for them to study when in hospital. It suggested that a 96-hour fortnight was the most any grade should work and that paid holidays were an absolute necessity. It suggested National and Regional Councils giving direct representation to organized nurses at which all the foregoing details could be discussed and agreed against local background.

The memorandum went into the conditions of health visitors; tuberculosis visitors, child life protection visitors, school nurses, district nurses, industrial nurses and midwives. The College insisted that all should be qualified nurses before taking training for these specialized posts and showed that under the existing system they were badly underpaid.

More encouragement to recruit men to enter nursing was

called for, and more training schools for them recommended. Better conditions in nurses' homes were pressed for in which there should always be a room for entertaining guests of either sex. Better food for nursing staffs and more facilities for recreation were asked together with more preliminary training schools. One point stressed above most others was that far too much use was being made of student and partly trained labour in wards. Fully trained nurses were mostly in the great city hospitals and the more rewarding forms of work. They were becoming expensive by management estimation. Therefore most of the provincial hospitals had to find their semi-skilled ward labour from probationers who had been unable to pass their examinations, and from the residue of those who had not even been able to gain registration as 'practising nurses' before 1925.

Essex County Council had struck against these conditions by boldly instituting training courses for nursing of the chronic sick by 'assistant nurses'.

On the subject of the partly trained the memorandum openly admitted that it was treading carefully. At that period existing nurses were afraid of the 'Essex' grade—irresponsible managements could employ them as cheap labour. Such an attitude was natural, and the College itself had always been against any reduction in training for those who would be entitled to use the title 'Nurse'. Nevertheless the shortage meant that the grade was immediately necessary, so the memorandum suggested that, to preserve the title 'Nurse', these partly trained workers should be called 'Attendants upon the Chronic Sick'.

Finally the memorandum deplored the fact that the General Nursing Council did not yet require that only qualified sister tutors should be employed in training schools.

The College was criticized however for its attitude to pay-rates for students as set forth in the memorandum: 'The payment of high salaries to student nurses is not recommended as it is believed that this does not tend to attract the most suitable type of candidate. The College prefers to regard the nurse in training as a student preparing for a career, receiving professional training practically free of cost and being provided with her maintenance when in hospital together with a small salary. The value of board, lodging, tuition, and medical attention given to student nurses is not always realized by parents and guardians, who are apt to have regard only to the monetary return obtainable for services.' (This received full agreement in the Athlone Committee's Report.) The College was strongly of the mind that the greatest need was to ensure that once the student was qualified she should receive an adequate salary.

Student nurses were in fact getting a far better and more profitable deal than apprentices in almost any other skilled craft or occupation. Such apprentices were usually only indentured after a considerable cash payment, following which they received neither board, lodging, nor medical attention, and their pay was about on a level with that of a student nurse.

Having regard to these parallel conditions the attitude of the College was beyond intelligent criticism. But criticism there was nevertheless as was only to be expected.

The Athlone Committee digested this mass of material with all other evidence and issued an Interim Report early in 1939. Owing to the fact that the Second World War broke out in September of that year the Committee suspended work and only one further report was produced. However, the effect of the immense investigation carried out by the College was that practically every one of its recommendations in the memorandum was adopted and repeated in the Committee's interim findings.

The main items of the Committee's Interim Report were:

(1) A committee should be established to regulate salaries of nurses in every grade on a national basis.

(2) A maximum of a 96-hours' fortnight should be worked by nurses and they should have four weeks leave every year.

(3) More domestic staff should be employed to relieve nurses of the daily repetition of routine tasks.

(4) Unreasonable rules and regulations affecting nurses' lives should be reviewed in the light of modern conditions.

(5) The policy of the profession in attempting to recruit nurses from secondary school girls was unrealistic because if the

figures were to be achieved it would absorb the whole yearly output from girls' secondary schools.

(6) As long as assistant nurses (whatever their title) worked in hospitals and other institutions under trained supervision their employment would be of great help to the community. A roll of such girls should therefore be established with a system of training. 'Existing nurses' should be admitted to the roll on a certificate of competence . . . and on evidence that they had practised the nursing of the sick for at least two years and were of good character.

(7) It should be made an offence for any agency or co-operation acting in connection with the employment of nurses to supply for gain the services of persons for the purpose of nursing the sick whose names are not entered on the Register or the Roll.

(8) *The Committee recommended that the Exchequer should give grants to the voluntary hospitals to enable them to increase nurses' pay.* In the view of the Committee the status of the nursing profession was all important and the profession should be recognized as a service of outstanding national importance.

This final recommendation was the epitaph of the voluntary system. The acceptance of Exchequer grants—public money raised through taxation—meant a measure of public control. The College had for years realized that it must come; the nursing profession now had to face it. The undeniable fact was that the voluntary system could not finance the progressive expansion of the nursing service—but no Government would pay out public money without demanding control of its spending.

The Government of the time was, however, embarrassed by the Committee's recommendation under this heading. Once Exchequer grants were agreed to they would form a precedent from which it would be impossible to retreat.

It all ended in a rather depressing anti-climax. The Government announced, despite the Athlone Report, that it was 'neither sound nor proper for the Government to make itself responsible for the payment of salaries to members of a particular profession'.

But the 'Essex' grade of 'assistant nurse' received a double blessing. The doctors were on her side.

The British Medical Association, as reported in the *Nursing Times*, stated that: 'There is no likelihood of replacing them (assistant nurses) by fully trained staff. Therefore it is highly desirable that their position should be defined and regularized, and a clear demarcation made, so that the public could readily distinguish between the trained nurse and the unqualified assistant.'

A great part of the work leading up to the massive memorandum presented to the Athlone Committee in 1938 had been carried out by one of the most energetic and able officers who had yet served the College in the twenty-two years of its history. This was Frances Goodall who had originally joined the staff as a part-time occupation when she was convalescing from an illness in 1928.

One of the most striking facts in the College history is the unusual good fortune it so constantly enjoyed in getting the right people for the right positions just when they were wanted. Mary Rundle let it be known that she wanted a first-class assistant, and when the Matron at Guy's Hospital telephoned to suggest Frances Goodall, she agreed to see her immediately.

Trained at Guy's Hospital, Frances Goodall held various positions at the Royal Masonic Hospital, Lewisham Hospital, and Moorfields Eye Hospital, and eventually returned to Guy's. She proceeded to overwork herself and fell ill. There followed a long and trying period of convalescence—especially trying to her nature for she had abounding vitality and hated inaction. Directly she was able to do so she applied to her Matron at Guy's for part-time work, but the Matron who knew her well believed that she had far greater capabilities than could be fully exploited in hospital work. Thus the introduction was made and Frances Goodall was appointed Assistant Secretary.

It was not long before Mary Rundle realized that she had received something like an answer to an executive's prayer. Frances Goodall took up the new work with intelligence, enterprise, and energy. In the years that followed she showed a genius for administration, and when Mary Rundle retired in

1933 she was appointed Secretary in succession. Later, the title
was altered to that of General Secretary.

As a negotiator she has had few equals in College history.
After the preparatory work on the memorandum for the
Athlone Committee she was intimately concerned with the
negotiations on the Rushcliffe* Committee on which she served
as one of the College representatives and later with the long
and complex negotiations throughout the planning stages of the
National Health Service† which came into being in 1948.

Thereafter Frances Goodall became Secretary of the Staff
Side of the Nurses and Midwives Whitley Council‡ which
negotiates conditions of service for all grades of nurses within
the National Health Service and was subsequently appointed
Staff Side Chairman. This position she continued to hold for
several years after her retirement from the General Secretaryship of the Royal College of Nursing in 1957.

Throughout her career Frances Goodall knew well that an
organization of the magnitude of the College needed the
expertise of big-business management. She had always worked
to bring College achievements to the notice of powerful people
and to gain their friendship and help.

Two of the most notable public men she was able to interest
in the College, and who thereafter played a great part in its
development, were Sir Frederick Leggett and Sir Frederic
Hooper. Sir Frederick Leggett was a gifted administrator
experienced in negotiation, who became Chairman of the
College Labour Relations Committee.

Sir Frederick brought to the task both a lively mind and a
well-weathered knowledge of top negotiation. He had been in
the Civil Service since 1904, Private Secretary to the Parliamentary Secretary of the Board of Trade in 1915, the same
position to the Minister of Labour in 1917, and Under-Secretary
to the Ministry in 1939. He was Chief Industrial Commissioner
in 1940, Deputy Secretary of the Ministry of Labour between
1942–45, and Chairman of the London Docks Disputes Inquiry
Committee in 1950. These are only illustrative details taken
from a very long list.

Sir Frederic Hooper became Chairman of the Finance

Committee of the Royal College in 1947. He was a man of quite astonishing variation of expertise. He was a B.Sc. and Fellow of University College, London, and earlier had been through the First World War in the tough conditions of an infantry regiment in the trenches. The list of his following achievements would fill pages of this book, but just a few will give an idea of both his administrative ability and versatility of mind.

He became Director of the Political Research Centre in 1942–44, Director of Business Training, Ministry of Labour, in 1945–46, Deputy Chairman of the Committee on Servicing Aspects of the Royal Air Force in 1955, and Chairman of the Regular Forces Resettlement Service, Ministry of Labour, in 1957–60. Amid dozens of varying commitments he was perhaps best known as Managing Director of the giant Schweppes Group of companies.

The shrewd guidance of such a man was of enormous value to the College, and was especially sustaining to Frances Goodall's successor as General Secretary. Catherine Hall, who still occupies that position, found in him a wise and valuable friend, especially in the early days of her administration.

Sir Frederic Hooper died in 1963 and was subsequently succeeded as Chairman of the College Finance Committee by Lord Silsoe, who had made a great name as Sir Arthur Malcolm Trustrum Eve, Q.C., G.B.E., M.C., T.D., a Bencher of the Inner Temple, and since 1954 First Church Commissioner.

CHAPTER NINETEEN

The Horder Committee

THE COUNCIL OF THE ROYAL COLLEGE was, naturally, disappointed that the Athlone Committee had been forced, owing to the war, to suspend work prematurely. So much that was immediately important had been left in the air. The Interim Report had recommended the grade of assistant nurse but had gone into no precise details. Finally, it had produced little more effect than a recommendation issued by the Ministry of Health that 'Local Authorities, in the light of the Athlone Report, should take such necessary action as was immediately possible without incurring additional expenditure'. The last four words quite obviously inhibited any action of real use.

The Athlone Committee finally issued a second report in 1945, on mental and mental-defective nursing. This recommended that there should be one accepted qualifying examination for the mental nurse, that is, the State Final Examination in Mental Nursing of the General Nursing Council. It also proposed that more mental nurses should serve on the Mental Nursing Committee of the General Nursing Council.

This was a strong report and the Council of the Royal College convened a conference in London where details of conditions of work, training, and post-certificate education of mental nurses were thrashed out by senior mental hospital doctors and nurses, and the conclusions forwarded to the Minister.

But to return to the Interim Report of 1939. The conditions of war were making demands upon nursing which it was obvious would increase. The Council of the College, realizing that reconstruction in the nursing world was essential if war and post-war demands were to be met, set up in 1941 a Committee, known as the Nursing Reconstruction Committee under the distinguished chairmanship of The Rt. Hon. Lord Horder, G.C.V.O., M.D., with the following terms of reference:

'To consider ways and means of implementing the recommendations of the interim report of the Inter-departmental Committee on Nursing Services and to recommend such further adjustments to the nursing services as the present situation and post-war reconstruction may demand.' This Committee was unique in that unlike any committee which had previously considered nursing problems on a national scale, at least half of its membership was composed of nurses. The remainder were appointed by kindred associations and included representatives of the medical profession, hospital and local authorities, hospital administrators, etc. The Committee held its inaugural meeting in November of that year when four sub-committees were set up to examine particular aspects of the problem. One of the first items for discussion was the question of the establishment of a grade of assistant nurse.

By the autumn of 1942 Section I of the Committee's Report —the Report on the Assistant Nurse—was published. In its opening paragraphs the Committee stated:

'The Assistant Nurse . . . should become one of the most stable elements in our National Nursing Service—an integral part of the Profession, and a person whose status offers the key to the improved training and employment of her senior partner, the State Registered Nurse.'

The Report made recommendations for the training, qualifications, employment and control of the assistant nurse, and included provisions for assistant nurses already in practice, for 'practising' nurses who had failed to register under the Act of 1919, provisions with regard to the control of nurse-supply agencies and for the closing of the profession to all but state registered or enrolled assistant nurses and those in training for such qualifications.

The Report received wide publicity and on the whole was welcomed by the profession. Ethel Bedford Fenwick was expected to fight the assistant nurse grade to the last ditch— and she did. But although she appeared alarmingly powerful with her British College of Nurses, and was a brilliant campaigner, she was doomed to failure by the economic facts of life.

In all, the Horder Committee issued four Reports and two supplementary Reports, the last being in 1949. The impact of its first Report was however soon apparent. In March 1943 the Minister of Health presented a Bill to Parliament which contained many of the recommendations of the Horder Report except that it contained no provisions for making nursing a closed profession. In April the Bill received Royal Assent and became the Nurses Act, 1943. Under this Act the General Nursing Council was required to form and keep a Roll of Assistant Nurses, make rules regarding the conditions of admission and the conduct of examinations for entry to the Roll. In addition, an Assistant Nurses Committee of the General Nursing Council was to be set up. Other provisions dealt with the registration and control of nurse-supply agencies. The Act finally made it a punishable offence for untrained persons to mislead anyone into thinking they had nursing qualifications. A similar Act—the Nurses (Scotland) Act, 1943 —received Royal Assent in August.

Towards the end of 1943 the Nursing Reconstruction Committee issued Sections II and III of its Report. Section II on Education and Training preceded that on Recruitment (Section III) as it was considered that the objective should be defined before discussing measures to secure candidates. Certain aspects of education including training of public health nurses and preparation for post-certificate qualifications were deferred in order not to delay publication and were the subject of later supplements. The Committee stated firmly that nursing should be regarded as an integral part of the national scheme for adult education, that student status should be safeguarded with a clear separation between the training of nurses and the obligation to provide nursing services for the patient; to achieve this end the income of the training school should be independent of the hospital. State aid was invoked to implement one of the most important recommendations of the Athlone Committee, namely that hospitals should receive financial assistance towards the cost of nursing education. Other recommendations were a wider basic training, the establishment of one Register, widespread changes in the training of the mental nurse, and reconstitution of the General

Nursing Councils. Recommendations with regard to planned recruitment on a national basis and for pre-nursing courses were outlined in Section III. Two supplements to Section II were issued in 1945: Minimum Standards for Nurse Training Schools and the Training of Public Health Nurses; and a third supplement early in 1946: Advanced Nursing Studies—an Aspect of Modern Adult Education.

The work on social and economic conditions which had been suspended in 1942 pending the results of various national inquiries was resumed in 1947. A comprehensive range of subjects was given detailed study and the work was not completed until late in 1949. This fourth and final Section of the Horder Committee's Report—the Social and Economic Conditions of the Nurse—was in the form of a survey, and unlike the other Sections contained no recommendations. The Report ranged from a study of what was meant by student status, to the part of the professional woman in public affairs. It discussed the indiscriminate demand for nursing care, the need to use alternative sources of help and to reserve the nurse for the work for which she had been trained. There were sections on prospects, conditions of service, joint consultation, and negotiation.

This Nursing Reconstruction Committee carried out what is perhaps one of the most important and comprehensive pieces of investigation for the nursing profession at a time of radical social change. It made far-reaching recommendations. Certain of these have been implemented, others have been overtaken by events, but a number have still to be achieved—real student status, complete financial independence for nursing education from hospital finances, clear demarcation between training needs and the needs of the nursing service, an increase in the number of enrolled nurses, and the proper utilization of nursing skills. All these have been reiterated in reports issued by the College over the years, in particular in the latest of these which appeared in 1964.*

* See p. 178, The Platt Report: *A Reform of Nursing Education.*

CHAPTER TWENTY

Second World War

AT THE declaration of war in September 1939, there had been estimated to be between fifty and sixty thousand trained nurses in the United Kingdom. But at the most conservative estimate (and with the known size of the enemy air arm), twice that number were likely to be needed. As a first measure it was decided to withdraw half the trained staff from all the civilian hospitals (when emergency dictated) which were to continue with a proportion of untrained women. The formation of the Civil Nursing Reserve attracted some ten thousand volunteers, three-quarters of whom were fully trained. The College was asked to undertake the recruitment of nurses for this Reserve and the keeping of the necessary records. In London this was carried out by the Secretary of the London Branch and in Scotland by the Secretary of the Scottish Board. These women, as the war developed, helped to staff the civilian and service hospitals and first-aid posts in the worst blitzed areas. Yet difficulties arose in the business of integrating the 'assistant nurses' or partly trained recruits into the still-rigid rank-consciousness of hospital life.

To add to this, the difficulty about the Voluntary Aid Detachment girls which had plagued nursing in the First World War, broke out all over again, as though there had been no interval of twenty years. Since there were nowhere near enough recruits the country had to have V.A.D. volunteers who were, again, for the most part drawn from the upper and middle social classes. They were given fifty hours 'training' upon entry.

As before, they were resented by trained nursing staff who —rightly from a professional point of view—rated them below assistant nurses in the matter of skill and experience. Yet in the early years of the war the V.A.D.s enjoyed 'officer' status.

They were, understandably, given only the most simple and menial of work about the wards, and naturally, they rebelled. By action of their very efficient Council, they were soon relieved of such tasks by edict of the War Office. This of course did not make them any more popular with the hospitals who were forced to employ more domestic staff.

The position of the V.A.D.s, however, was untenable alongside women of full training and experience, so that in 1943 the only thing possible was done, and their 'officer status' was withdrawn. Thenceforth they worked like any other virtually untrained volunteers in any of the Services—and in the course of the war demonstrated great value in devotion and courage. The V.A.D.s, however, again got far more publicity in the illustrated papers than the trained nurses because in so many cases their social background made what Fleet Street calls 'news'.

The *Nursing Times* put it bluntly in 1943: 'How often do we see photographs printed in the national Press showing men of the Forces, and casualties in civilian life, being attended in bed by a young girl with a cross on her cap and on her bosom—and the public is too often left to assume that this cross is an essential part of the nurse's uniform.'

Incredible though it seems, these embellishments remained part of the V.A.D. uniform throughout the war, their only effect being to give those who had to wear them a bad odour with their professional seniors. Moreover the publicity always tended to detract from the really excellent work done by so many of them.

As the first almost inactive months of the war dragged on the nursing shortage was solved in a way no one had ever dreamed of—solved temporarily, in any case. Since no flow of casualties came in, the hospitals concerned were heavily over-staffed in reference to occupied beds.

Meanwhile emergency hospitals were set up in large numbers, and were staffed by the available trained staff drawn from the existing hospitals, and by assistants, V.A.D.s, and student nurses. But there were practically no patients! Even so, the Ministry of Health believed that when the fighting really started they would find the hospitals understaffed—and they were right. When the storm broke the hospitals and their staffs suffered heavily from the intensive bombing.

Meanwhile a big and well-conducted publicity campaign was carried out to attract recruits. The campaign was successful, a large factor being that women already knew that they were facing conscription into the Services or the factories. A good number of them therefore volunteered for nursing, probably not realizing the hardness of the work and long hours involved—much longer than any wartime schedules in factories.

Nurses were never conscripted. The profession was and always will be a voluntary and vocational occupation because it would be impossible to make a useful nurse out of an unwilling entrant. The country wanted nurses—partly trained or untrained as it had to be—but not women who would be of no use in hospital emergencies. The V.A.D.s, for all their shortcomings (in some opinions), had volunteered for nursing and wanted to nurse, although they did not relish the work that any student nurse had to do in her early years. Assistant nurses at this period—and throughout the war—proved themselves to be invaluable.

In 1943, when the full shock of war had smashed down upon the country and had been endured by the civilian population without any sign of break, the nursing shortage was again a major problem by reason of both civilian and nursing casualties. Therefore the Government had to ordain that any woman between the ages of seventeen and sixty who had had nursing experience in the preceding ten years must register with the Ministry of Labour. Later in the same year, nurses and midwives between eighteen and forty years old were only allowed to leave whatever professional work they were doing if they went to other employment in a field of nursing shortage. This was under the Control of Engagements Order, 1943 under which those requiring nurses could only obtain them through a Ministry of Labour Appointments Board, and nurses requiring appointments could only obtain them through the same source. There was, however, a loophole by which nurses could leave whatever they were doing if they took up extended training.

These measures were the nearest the nursing profession has

ever come to anything savouring of autocratic control (beyond
their own senior ranks), but even so it did not prove a success.
The system was tightened later and newly trained nurses
could be directed wherever they were needed. Again this was
not unduly resented since all nurses rightly regarded themselves as being in the uniformed service of the country. But it
did not succeed as far as had been hoped because many
women who did not like their 'postings' took the loophole still
available and applied for further training.

The College had for many years pressed for the establishment
of a Division of Nursing at the Ministry of Health but without
success. In view of the heavy demands being made on the
nursing services as a result of the war, the Council, in January
1941, passed the following resolution, which was released to the
Press and received wide publicity:

'In view of the increasing number of matters concerning
nurses and nursing coming under the control of the Ministry
of Health . . . and in order to deal with possible changes in the
health services as a result of the war, the Royal College of
Nursing urges that pressure be brought to bear on the Minister
of Health to establish within the Ministry a department of
nursing administered and staffed by suitably trained and
experienced members of the nursing profession.'

Miss Irene Ward, M.P., stressed the urgency of such a
department in the House of Commons during the debate on
woman power in the following March. As a result the Parliamentary Secretary to the Ministry of Health, Miss Florence
Horsburgh, M.P. announced on the same day that the Minister
had agreed to the step.

After an informal conference to which the Minister invited
representatives of the College, the outline of the new department
was agreed in principle, and the recruitment of nurses and
superannuation followed as points of discussion. Next day, in
the House of Commons, the Minister not only announced the
formation of the Nursing Division of the Ministry of Health but
also made an appeal for nursing recruits, promising students
who enrolled at hospitals recognized as training schools salaries

of £40 per annum rising by a yearly £5. He also announced rises of salaries for trained nurses, assistant nurses, and auxiliary nurses who were members of the Civil Nursing Reserve which had been formed at the outbreak of war. Further, he urged hospital authorities in general to review the salaries of their nursing staffs in view of the increases he had just authorized. The Minister also announced that Miss K. C. Watt, C.B.E., R.R.C., Principal Matron for the Emergency Nursing Services since 1939, had been appointed Chief Nursing Officer of the new Ministry Division. Later Miss Watt was joined by two assistants, Miss M. G. Lawson and Miss M. E. Flambert.

CHAPTER TWENTY-ONE

The Rushcliffe Committee

IT WILL be remembered that one of the recommendations in the College memorandum to the Inter-departmental Committee on Nursing Services was the setting up of national and regional councils to negotiate salaries and conditions for nurses. A draft scheme was drawn up and conferences arranged with Government Departments and other bodies. The outbreak of war suspended any action that might have been taken to implement the reforms recommended in the Committee's Interim Report including the establishment of negotiating machinery. In 1940, however, the College was able to announce that as a result of prolonged negotiation, but as an interim measure only, a Local Authorities Nursing Services Joint Committee was to be set up to deal with the conditions of nurses employed by local authorities, hoping that this might be the first step towards promoting negotiating machinery for the whole profession.

In 1941 the Minister of Health announced the setting up of a Nurses Salaries Committee (the Rushcliffe Committee) which would consist of an employers' panel and a nurses' panel and would deal with salaries only. The College view was that hours and conditions of work demanded as much reform as salaries, and that therefore all three subjects should be considered together. The Minister, however, refused to agree with a request carried by a deputation from the Local Authorities Nursing Services Joint Committee (which included representatives of the College) that the proposed committee should be on Whitley Council lines, to cover the broader field. He insisted that the new Committee's terms of reference would be on salaries only, but invited nine members of the College to serve upon the nurses' panel. The College accepted but in doing so stated that they would still press for the Whitley Council type of negotiating machinery for the nursing profession when opportunity allowed. At the same time the Secretary of State for Scotland set up a similar Committee under Professor T. M. Taylor with the same basis of representation. On this Committee the first Chairman of the Nurses' Panel was one of the representatives of the College.

The Committees started their work in October 1941 with the direction that they should draw up agreed scales of salaries and emoluments for the state registered nurses employed respectively in England and Wales or in Scotland in hospitals and public health services, and for student nurses in hospitals approved as training schools by the General Nursing Council. It was to be a triumph for the College that these terms of reference were, after all, early in 1942 amended to include conditions of service. The Minister had at last agreed to this in view of representations received from both the employers' and nurses' panels. As a result the Local Authorities Nursing Services Joint Committee agreed to suspend activities until such time as the Rushcliffe Committee made a report.

Both Committees issued their first two reports in 1943, recommending salary scales and certain conditions for nurses in hospital and for public health and district nurses. With regard to student nurses the Rushcliffe Committee stated: 'The student nurse should be regarded primarily as a student who is receiving a valuable training, with tuition from medical as well as nursing staff, although at the same time she is helping to staff her hospital. . . . In other professions it is customary for the student to pay fees for training; the student nurse not only receives hers free but in addition is paid a salary . . . what is chiefly required . . . is that the prospects of the nurse after training in senior as well as junior posts should be equable and attractive.' This had been the policy of the College for many years.

The Committee then recommended rises for all ranks from 'assistant nurse' upwards but, having regard to the wartime rocketing of prices, the extra granted made very little difference to the recipients. The maximum recommended hours were ninety-six per fortnight ('as soon as circumstances permit'); one day off per week was laid down together with twenty-eight days paid leave per year. Sick pay was to run from one to three

Rcn Headquarters, London

Rcn Scottish Headquarters, Edinburgh

Photo: Photo Illustra

Left: Rcn Northern Ireland
Headquarters, Belfast

Photo: W. D. Fry

Below: Rcn Welsh
Headquarters, Cardiff

Photo: Hill's Welsh Press

Above: A corner of the Library at Rcn Headquarters, London

Below: Students from many lands attend courses at the Rcn. A group with their tutor at one entrance to the London Headquarters.

Photo: Photo Repartage

months according to length of service. Night duty was to be limited to six months for sisters and staff nurses and three months for students.

The 'assistant nurse' was officially accepted by the Rushcliffe Committee and her salary rate laid down. There was some anomaly here since the Civil Nursing Reserve (formed in 1939) had had assistant nurses since it started, and their qualification had been put at two years' 'experience' before joining the Reserve. These were to continue but in future new assistant nurses were required to do two years' hospital training, although not necessarily in hospitals recognized as training schools by the General Nursing Councils. The Committee continued the traditional system of paying nurses 'net' salaries. Those who lived-in received their board, lodging, and other benefits ('emoluments') plus salary. Those who lived out received in addition to salary a living-out allowance. There was also a system for calculating what proportion of the whole rated for superannuation.

In short, everything that really mattered in the Athlone Report was adopted but . . . once again the Rushcliffe Committee like its predecessors made nothing compulsory. It did make one stride forward, however, beyond anything that had been done before. It announced that the Government would pay half the cost of any increase in expenditure (estimated at £1½–£2 million) of implementing the proposals it recommended to voluntary and local-authority hospitals.

Probably these decisions would have been coloured had those concerned possessed the clairvoyance to know that the National Health Service was only five years in the future. Already plans were tentatively being discussed behind the scenes politically. 'Nationalization' of the whole medical profession appeared inevitable to realists since, after Rushcliffe, Government control of the voluntary hospitals was already half in being since public money was paying much of their cost. The thin end of the wedge had been admitted—there having been no possible way of stopping it.

CHAPTER TWENTY-TWO

National Health Service—All-Party Plan 1944

DELICATE NEGOTIATIONS followed the Nurses Act of 1943 in which there was a clause which prevented those who practised as Christian Science nurses from using the title 'nurse'.

Christian Scientists had understandably been active in trying to get this clause revoked. As far as religious tenets are concerned the College believed in complete individual freedom. In regard to Christian Science, however, the Council found itself in the same difficulty as the rest of the qualified medical profession.

The law of the land (in simple, layman's terms) states that no one may take his or her own life or, by denying available medical care, put any in danger of their lives.

It is obvious that no qualified nurse would be justified in refusing or disobeying qualified medical advice whatever her personal religious beliefs might be. Further, the College could recognize no form of religious training as being a substitute for the hospital training required by the General Nursing Council.

The College, therefore, had a bounden duty to the general public to ensure that the word 'nurse' should not be used by Christian Science practitioners unless they had taken the full normal training for registration. The College had, and has, no concern with what anyone may believe. It was concerned only with its practical duty to ensure that when the public needed a nurse, only nurses trained by the approved system should be available.

The struggle was not easy. The cry of religious intolerance was raised although it had nothing to do with the issue, as has been explained.

In any case the College was relieved when the matter was settled and Christian Science attendants who were not qualified nurses were precluded from using the word 'nurse'.

The College also pointed out to the Minister of Health that there were various people who would be unfairly prevented from enrolling on the National Register under the 1943 Act by the existing time-limit laid down by the General Nursing Council. These included nurses of both sexes who had become prisoners of war, or who were serving in remote parts of the war-theatre where communications were uncertain. The Ministry forthwith announced new regulations to cover these cases.

In February of the following year, 1944, the Coalition Government issued through the Ministry of Health a White Paper on a National Health Service. It had been known that the all-party Government under the then Mr. Winston Churchill, had been preparing the plan of a service of the kind and the College had been very active in contacting all branches of the nursing interest, particularly through its own organization to gather opinion on the subject.

From the nursing point of view the White Paper was a disappointment. Importance was given to the provision of a complete domiciliary nursing service, but there was little recognition of the fact that the success of the public health, hospital, and clinical services depended on whether there was an adequate supply of well-trained nurses to carry them out.

The College drew up draft memoranda on a 'Plan of Nursing in a National Health Service' which formed the basis of discussion at the Annual Conference that year. At this several Government officials were present, and the then Minister of Health, the Rt. Hon. H. U. Willink, K.C., M.P., gave the inaugural address.

The Conference stressed the need to develop all branches of nursing in relation to the National Health Service from a base of general and professional education. It dealt with the importance of expanding the domiciliary nursing service to include, where necessary, a full-time as well as a visiting service. Health centres were proposed with more comprehensive functions than the grouped medical practices outlined in the White Paper. Schemes were outlined for co-ordinating public health and institutional nursing policy within each local government area; and for improving in various other ways the preventive and curative health service which should be the right of every citizen.

The chief emphasis, however, was on the importance of adequate national and local machinery for the nursing and midwifery professions to have direct access to the Minister, and to give technical advice on professional matters connected with the carrying out of a National Health Service.

On 2 May the Minister of Health received a deputation from the College. The most important part of the discussion concerned the fact that if the student status of the nurse in training was to be fully acknowledged, hospitals must receive financial assistance from national funds for educational work undertaken as recommended in the Athlone and Horder Reports. The deputation also asked for clarification of the suggestion in the Rushcliffe Report that the General Nursing Council should regularize the position of certificates in different branches of nursing awarded by various bodies to ensure official recognition by that Council in suitable cases.

The College representatives referred to the extent of educational activities it was empowered to promote and explained that these powers had been used in full and had so far been undisputed. They pointed out to the Minister that should any Amending Act of Parliament give the General Nursing Council the right to direct future post-certificate education of nurses it would deprive the College of one of the most important functions of its Royal Charter.

The Minister said he would arrange for the matter to be explored with the General Nursing Council, but felt it was intended that the latter should deal with such post-certificate education as involved training in hospitals.

The College representatives also referred to the proposed payment of educational grants to hospital authorities prepared to assist nurses to become sister tutors. They pointed out that the method suggested (i.e. of paying a grant equivalent to half of the expenditure involved) was not acceptable because it might induce hospitals, in their anxiety to obtain the services of qualified sister tutors, to choose members of their own staff who had hitherto no intention of teaching, and who might possibly take a course solely for reasons of promotion. Moreover, these grants carried certain obligations, one being that the recipients should undertake to serve for a specified period.

The College felt this might militate against a nurse's interest and suggested that students should not be tied to fulfil any contract of service in any particular hospital, but that the condition should only require the student to *teach* for one year, and so be free to choose where that teaching should take place.

Alternatively, it was suggested that grants should be made direct to the individual, particularly as the student was more often than not interested in teaching for its own sake. They recommended a scheme similar to that dealing with 'training and resettlement of disabled persons' as suitable for adoption.

Later in the year the College agreed with the Ministry draft regulations on the control of supply agencies. These required that the nurse in charge of any agency must be registered on the general part of the State Register; nurses holding special qualifications should in every case be used solely for work for which they were qualified; every agency *must* inform every patient as to the qualifications of nurses; agencies must keep records for the inspector—who must be a State Registered nurse—to verify that only suitably qualified nurses were supplied.

In general, however, the College let it be known that it was 'apprehensive' of details in the White Paper which made it plain that so many nursing services were to be brought under local government. As events were to prove, the College views and suggestions were to have a great effect upon the shape of the National Health Service when it was brought into being four years later. Meanwhile, with the victorious end of the war in 1945, the year following the publication of the White Paper, and the advent of a General Election, a Labour Government was returned to power. Thus it became the Labour Minister of Health, the late Aneurin Bevan, who was destined to reframe the first all-party conception of the National Health Service into the form by which it became law.

The end of the year 1945 was marked by a spectacular misunderstanding of the nurses' outlook and ideals by a number of local authorities. These passed resolutions requiring that all their employees should become members of trade unions. For the most part the nurses and assistant nurses insisted upon their right to join whatever nursing organization they liked, whether it was a trade union or not.

The Willesden Borough Council, however, tried to force the issue by issuing dismissal notices to those on their staff who refused to comply with the demand within a specified time. About eighty per cent of these were members of the Royal College of Nursing or its Student Nurses Association. In indignation they turned to the College which promised them all help; meanwhile they were advised to act in a strictly professional manner and stand by their patients. Which they all did.

The immediate difficulty appeared to be that, owing to the Government's repeal of the Trades Disputes and Trade Unions Act of 1927, the Willesden Council might have a legal right to the course it had taken. However, when the College came to take up the nurses' case it found the battle already more than half won.

The Willesden Council's action had, naturally, been front-page news in papers from one end of the country to the other. As a result ordinary common-sense people read about it and talked about it. Quite clearly in the general public view the Willesden and similar local councils had gone too far; they had lost sight of the fact that a dedicated and highly skilled woman has a will of her own.

The net result was a burst of ridicule from the Press followed by statements in turn by three Ministers of the Government, in rising order of seniority. As a result the whole thing collapsed like a pricked balloon. The Willesden Borough Council announced that it was suspending all action upon the resolutions and that the dismissed nurses would be reinstated. In short the ordinary people of Britain had acted as illogically (and sensibly) as they usually do on an important issue.

The nurse has a special place in the country's heart and when it came to nurses being pushed around and told what to do—especially by such favourites of comedians as local bigwigs—then the country became genuinely angry and was prepared to do something about it. The leaders in power were clear-headed and shrewd; they realized the danger, and acted accordingly.

The College made no claim to a triumph which belonged to the people at large. However, since the members of a profession had had their right to be represented by their professional organization challenged, the College felt that the time had come for a clearing of the air. The following statement was therefore issued to all State Registered Nurses:

'The Royal College of Nursing supports—and has always supported—the view that under modern conditions nurses should be organized on a national basis, but feels equally that each nurse should be free to choose for herself the particular organization to which she would like to belong, and which she feels is best able to meet her professional needs . . .

'Affiliated to and working closely with the College are the Association of Sick Children's Hospital Nurses and the Society of Registered Male Nurses. The pre-eminent position of the Royal College in the nursing world receives practical recognition from the Government who have given the Royal College far more places on the Nurses Panel of the Rushcliffe and Whitley Committees on nurses' salaries and conditions than have been allotted to any other organization.

'But, however well fitted by its nature and constitution the Royal College may be, the success with which it can work for the interests of nurses and of the profession depends upon having the widest possible membership among nurses. Only so can it speak with the fullest authority and continue to build-up the benefits and privileges which its membership can offer.'

If there was here a little beating of the College drum it was justified, and certainly a healthy note at a time of discord. The Council insisted then and at all times that the College was non-political. So long as nurses did their professional duty by their patients and refused for any reason to leave them without care, it mattered not what political party any of them might favour. For their own sakes and for the profession at large, however, the College was prepared to fight any attempt by anyone to force nurses to join organizations which did not appeal to them.

By the end of the year the College was engaged again in

purely professional matters. Since the end of the war it had
been trying to secure Government grants for nurses demobilized
from service in the Forces. The case was good not only from a
point of view of fairness, but by comparison with action taken
by the Government in other ways since coming to power.
Under the Scheme for Further Education and Training,
Government grants were offered to those whose careers had
been interrupted by their war service. The College claimed
that many nurses came into this category.

To this the Government would not agree. It was insisted
that a nurse could automatically obtain further education and
training directly she went back to work in a hospital ward.
Nurses' claims under the Scheme were therefore refused.

In the same way the College's request for grants for refresher
courses for nurses were turned down although the Government
had made provision for doctors and dentists in this respect in
the White Paper on the National Health Service. The College,
however, was able to have the matter raised in the House of
Lords, as a result of which the Government spokesman gave an
assurance that nurses would be included in the provision.

CHAPTER TWENTY-THREE

The Royal College and the National Health Service

THE MINISTER OF HEALTH, Aneurin Bevan, issued new proposals about the National Health Service early in 1946 which showed that after consideration of the College's views, he was prepared to take a more realistic attitude to the part the profession of nursing had to play. The new proposals were very different from those of the White Paper of 1944 and the College found it had got agreement to many of its suggestions.

The demand that the nursing profession should have its own Standing Advisory Committee at national level with direct access to the Minister had been granted. On the other hand the College Council was still worried that the proposals would not give adequate nurse representation at regional and local levels where it was obvious that nursing would have an important administrative part to play.

One of the Council's main objections to the 1944 White Paper had been that so many nursing services were scheduled to be brought under local government. These objections were met in the amended scheme whereby the Minister, working through regional boards based on university medical teaching centres, would take over all hospitals. The College believed that this arrangement would lead to closer co-ordination between the mental and physical health services and would facilitate and improve nurse training; further, that it would obviate overlapping and lead to a more economic use of small hospitals, and improve institutional care of long-stay and chronic cases.

As far as local administration was concerned the College was in favour of the retention of the local-government mechanism at county and borough level for the conduct of the clinic,

10

welfare, and domiciliary services. This was because regional control over these services, so intimate to the areas concerned, would clearly be too remote. Overall, however, the College still believed that the existing system of local government should be examined in detail and drastically overhauled. The great danger feared was the 'bumbledom' which had been so often the curse of local administration.

So long as this danger was appreciated by the Minister, and measures were taken to obviate it, the College was well pleased with the new outline of the service. That there had to be such a service, brought about by whatever party had gained power, was beyond question.

As things had turned out it was generally felt that the measure could have been very much worse. One of the most welcome decisions was that the teaching hospitals were to be left with considerable autonomy. Beyond this everyone was relieved that the welfare services were to be extended, and that the overall plans for England, Wales, and Scotland were to be almost identical.

Whether or not 'Nye' Bevan's politics were acceptable to whoever had dealings with him, the estimation of his abilities was always the same. He was a man of brilliant mind and forceful personality; imaginative, mercurial—and stubborn. His sincerity to his own cause was almost fanatical. Therefore when, in February of the year, he invited representatives of the College and five other nursing organizations to 'discuss the shape of the final proposals' with him and the Secretary of State for Scotland, there was a feeling that this was more polite window-dressing than a request for genuine discussion. Since Mr. Bevan had built his Act upon the best professional advice he could get he believed in it passionately, and was not likely to brook interference.

At the meeting, however, he proved to be far more flexible than had been feared. He listened carefully to all the views for which he had asked, and was clearly giving them full consideration. The fact was that, having settled the rest of the scheme, he genuinely wanted to incorporate nursing into it in the most efficient way possible, and he had come to the people who could tell him how. Even so, his typical obstinacy showed when he refused to consider professional nurse representation on regional boards or local committees—only that of doctors and dentists.

Just why he would not admit even experienced matrons in those cases it is difficult to judge. But with his usual quickness of mind he pointed out that there was nothing to prevent trained nurses finding themselves on such bodies on the grounds of their individual merits.

Under the draft proposals he was empowered to make regulations for superannuation of nurses and other officers—a matter close to the heart of the College, the Council of which was pleased by the request for nomination of a panel of nurses to discuss the matter.

By this time the College had already four members on the National Advisory Committee which forwarded to the Minister its findings on assistant nurse training schools, pre-nursing courses, the nursing of the chronic sick, and the staffing of public-assistance inititutions. The desirability of admitting displaced persons from Germany to nursing training was considered together with arrangements whereby nursing orderlies from the Services might be admitted to intensive courses of training for state registration.

The College meanwhile was not prepared to put up with the exclusion of nurses on regional hospital boards and committees to be set up under the new service—and it won its point in the next year, 1947. Further experience of Mr. Bevan's character showed the College negotiators that he had too high-grade an intelligence to allow political views to overcome practical common sense. Show him that any measure was right, necessary for the well-being of the greatest number, and on cool reflection he would agree to it even if it had been proposed by a political opponent.

The negotiators had learned more; when not in full vitriolic cry upon a platform, Bevan was studious and thoughtful. He personally studied and thought over every detail and item of the measure he passionately regarded as his own child and creation. Nothing framed by any expert or minor official was allowed to pass without his consideration. He was determined that the National Health Service—although originally an all-party concept—was to succeed from its first day because it had been finally detailed by a Government of his own party.

The College pressed repeatedly and tirelessly that trained nurses should serve on the regional hospital boards and committees, and put forward clear and obvious reasons why. Finally, Bevan reconsidered the position. The reason why he did was no change of heart. It was just part of his determination that the National Health Service must be made to work efficiently. What he had to guard against was the sort of criticism that could prove that any part of it had been designed without real consideration of public well-being, purely for political ends.

In the controversy with the College about nurse representation he realized at last that, in the public interest, he had been wrong and they were right. Since there was a nursing shortage which his experts assured him could not be solved for years, there would be acute problems of nursing facing every regional board and committee. To deal with this the advice and guidance of a trained and experienced nurse was an obvious necessity in every case. Such problems could not be settled successfully by doctors, far less by well-meaning but unqualified lay members, however experienced they might be in business affairs and general administration.

The outcome was that Bevan, after a little face-saving in which he suggested 'advisory machinery', finally announced that he had decided to consider the names of any suitable nurses the Council might suggest. Naturally the Council was ready with such names and sent them in promptly. Thus nurses were at last appointed to serve on regional hospital boards in England and Wales, and on the boards set up in Scotland. Of the nineteen nurses so chosen by Mr. Bevan all but one were members of the Royal College of Nursing.

It was typical of him, however, that he added a proviso. The appointed nurses were to serve in a purely individual capacity and were 'not to represent any organization'. But since, in practical terms, such a prohibition meant nothing, because nobody had asked for the denied licence, everybody concerned was satisfied.

In all ways the year 1947, the last year before the actual

implementation of the National Health Service, was one of intense activity for the College.

One of the most important matters to be settled was the superannuation scheme for all employed within the N.H.S., proposed by Mr. Bevan who issued draft regulations. The College, of course, had been active for years in making recommendations on this subject, and expected tough final negotiations. Somewhat to the surprise—and greatly to the gratification —of the Council, the Minister's draft regulations proved more satisfactory than any other scheme previously offered to the nursing profession. In fact the College's often-stated points of view had been most adequately met. Naturally, there were small points of detail upon which the Council submitted comments and suggestions. When the final draft was issued, however, there was no need for further discussion. The Minister had prepared an explanatory leaflet for the guidance of staffs in voluntary hospitals which he sent to the College for examination, and which was in all essentials satisfactory.

Work and correspondence concerning the new National Insurance Act as it affected nurses was extremely heavy. Many new regulations on the matter were drafted by the Government during the year and each had to be carefully studied by the College and the expert advisers it enlisted, and the necessary objections lodged. In addition, the Council were invited to give evidence to the Inter-departmental Committee on Industrial Diseases which the Ministry of Pensions and National Insurance set up to investigate questions concerning compensation.

This of course called for expert, on-the-spot reports, careful framing of material submitted, and equally careful consideration of the numerous anomalies in compensation which at that time existed. In addition the College had to cope with an almost endless stream of inquiries from individual members on this subject. Naturally, every member had a prescriptive right to information, but the load of work borne by everyone on the headquarters staff was heavy.

The College was solidly established as a platform upon which Government officials willingly and constantly came to meet nursing representatives to thrash out problems that were their joint concern. Every meeting had to be carefully supervised, nursing representatives briefed, all relative documents consulted, objective points settled.

At the same time the College had organized itself into a clearing-house where information from Government Departments regarding their new machinery could be recirculated throughout its nation-wide membership.

At such a period when the medical and nursing professions were in the final stages preceding new-birth, the work of dealing with every problem and every contingency was immense. Mr. Bevan was by no means the only one who wanted efficient results. All experienced nurses and doctors knew well that once regulations pass into law a very tedious time must pass before they are likely to be altered by any Government of any party. The reason being that all Governments, once they are in power, find themselves faced with far more business than they can deal with.

The year 1947 therefore was, from the practical point of view, probably the greatest year in the history of the College. In that year it carried more vital responsibility to the nursing profession; it achieved more by reason of the number of matters dealt with.

CHAPTER TWENTY-FOUR

The Passing of a Great Campaigner

As A result of the shortage of nurses, a working party had been set up in 1946 by the Ministry of Health, the Department of Health for Scotland, and the Ministry of Labour and National Service on the recruitment and training of nurses. Its terms of reference were 'to determine the proper task of the nurses; the training necessary to equip her for the task; the necessary annual intake to maintain an efficient nursing service—and how it was to be obtained; from what groups of the population nurses should be recruited; how to cut wastage'.

The working party, under the Chairmanship of Sir Robert Wood, was made up of a doctor, a psychologist, and two qualified nurses. Its report was issued in 1947, the main recommendations being:

Existing nurse-training schools were for the most part too small and many were without adequate clinical equipment, material or sister tutors;

A nurse-training board should be set up for each hospital region under a regional director of training with a permanent staff;

The finances of nurse training should be entirely separated from hospital finances; students should not be under the control of hospitals (except when undergoing training in the wards) but should be under the training authority;

Student nurses should be relieved of all domestic work for which no nursing training was necessary; if this was done two years' training could be substituted for three;

Full student status was necessary; students should not be treated as junior employees providing cheap labour;

Wastage—partly trained and trained nurses leaving the profession—was largely due to outdated forms of discipline, the unnecessarily harsh attitude of senior staff to juniors, the quality of food, the too-long hours, and the insistence on menial forms of work;

The position of the existing assistant nurse should be entirely reconsidered. No more assistants should be recruited but a new grade of nursing orderly should take their place.

As might have been expected the General Nursing Council issued a reply that was somewhat peremptory. The Council declared itself uncompromisingly against the suggested reduction of training time from three years to two, against the dropping of the assistant nurse grade, and against the separation of nurse-training finances from those of hospitals. It insisted upon retaining its own authority over all nurse training and examination.

In a minority report Dr. Cohen, a psychologist, announced that they had found insufficient evidence to decide upon the number of nurses that would be required, or the type of training most to be recommended. He suggested that the General Nursing Council should be reconsidered as to its present and future work, and that training and examination of nurses should be the responsibility of Divisions of Nursing at Health Departments.

None of these endeared him to the General Nursing Council of the time, but the fact was that many of his ideas and those put forward by the working-party majority were very much to the point, but before their time. Indeed the interest of the report lies in the fact that its main recommendations were destined to be repeated in the most modern of all blueprints for the future of the nursing profession.*

This year of the Wood Report, 1947, proved to be the last of Ethel Bedford Fenwick's brilliant and turbulent life. She was then ninety, but had kept her mental faculties and her magnificent energy of spirit to the end which came on 13 March.

In the words of an obituary writer: 'She was absolutely without fear, was dogged, tenacious, proud, and possessed thoroughly sound common sense. She could never suffer fools

* See p. 178.

gladly, and disloyalty or cowardice in word or deed were anathema to her.'

To these words which were true enough one may only add that her common sense was as sound as the best except when she was baulked or outmanoeuvred; then her fighting spirit would override it. She did an immense amount of good for nursing, to which she was utterly dedicated. It was said of her, probably with truth, that had she been born a man she would have become Prime Minister.

Such forceful, gifted, and dominating characters as she are not born in every generation, but it is a peculiarity of history that a single generation sometimes produces several. Had she not lived in an age of giants in her chosen profession, there is no doubt that she would have made herself its only acknowledged leader. As things happened, in her last days, she felt that she had been deserted by many of her followers who had realized at last that so much for which she still fought stubbornly was impractical.

As is the lot of so many aged people, Ethel Bedford Fenwick slipped and broke her thigh when she was 89. She was taken to Bart's, her own old hospital, but in spite of all that could be done she died some months after her ninetieth birthday. To the end, fortunately, there were certain of her pupils who were unquestioningly loyal and refused to observe any impracticalities in her policy. The obituary writer already mentioned continued:

'. . . Strange it was that so great a reformer, the bestower of so many good things upon nurses, should receive so little gratitude from them. Her tremendous efforts on their behalf received scant appreciation from her colleagues, yet she zealously continued along her chosen path, often maligned, always eventually justified in her actions and decisions . . . like a true prophet she has little honour in her own country but the wise Americans know, love, and honour her and so do the nurses of many other lands. . . .'

It is pleasant to record that this is true of America where the real value of her work was never marred by opposition, with the result that her judgement was affected by no distractions.

A final quote from one of her most unshakeably faithful followers gives a vivid picture of her character. Miss Hardie, who was about to represent her at the Congress of American Nurses at Atlantic City, wrote:

'I was one of the last persons to talk to Mrs. Bedford Fenwick before she died. I went to see her one cold, mid-winter afternoon, and when I saw her I knew she would not be long with us. But her eyes were bright and her intellect keen. For a while I chatted to the grand old lady but she soon tired and fell into a restless sleep. Then she awoke and said impatiently: "Now Miss Hardie, I hope you know how to make all arrangements for travelling to New York?"

'All the old authority had crept back into her voice which could still thrill one. I assured her that all arrangements were already made. She seemed taken aback for a moment and was obviously not pleased that we had managed to get along without her. Then she gave me a very penetrating glance and said: "Very well, I see that you have all managed very well without me, so you won't be requiring any further advice."

'She closed her eyes and seemed disinclined for further talk. I thought that she was sleeping and tried to steal very quietly out of the room. She opened her eyes just as I was going. "All right don't stay any longer now, Miss Hardie," she said. "You don't need me. None of you need me any more. Come and see me when you've time."

'She looked so old and frail and so very pathetic . . . I bent to kiss her forehead for I loved her and admired her greatly. She seemed pleased, and then I left her. Two days later she died. She had, as a last tribute to her beloved nursing profession, signed cheques totalling £2,000 to pay the expenses of some of her nurses to America . . .'

Perhaps that is a fitting point at which to leave the story of a very great personality.

CHAPTER TWENTY-FIVE

N.H.S. and Whitley Councils

UNDER THE National Health Service Act, 1946, which came into operation on 5 July 1948, the Minister was empowered to set up negotiating machinery to deal with salaries and conditions of service for all employees in the Health Service. After discussion it was agreed that this should take the form of Whitley Councils which still bear the name of the chairman of the first one set up in 1917, Mr. J. H. Whitley, later Speaker of the House of Commons, 'whereby problems, disputes, and disagreements could be settled by discussion and negotiation between representatives of the people concerned'. Separate Whitley Councils were set up to cover the different groups of employees, each Council consisting of a Management Side and a Staff Side.

On the Staff Side of the Nurses and Midwives' Whitley Council, the Royal College of Nursing was allotted twelve out of the forty-one seats, the largest number for any one organization.

But the new Health Service immediately ran into trouble. All nurses hitherto had enjoyed, as part of their condition of employment, free medical treatment. Now, however, student nurses, in common with all other grades, were called upon to pay National Insurance contributions, then 1s. 4d. per week. In July this was increased to 3s. 10d. per week—and as might have been expected uproar broke out.

The profession had put up with suddenly having to pay for what it had every reason to regard as a right. Partly this acquiescence was because the profession as a whole wanted to make the service work, and recognized it as a national need which the Government would have to fulfil; equally it was because nurses are by nature more interested in their work than in agitation.

But the young of any profession are naturally more inclined to rebellion than the old; moreover for a yearly £6. 10s. to be knocked off a student's meagre £70 was ridiculously out of proportion. As a result, student nurses all over the country either handed in notices to leave, or threatened to do so. Both the nursing and the national Press were on their side. One of the trade unions suggested a public demonstration. On the day chosen, the Sunday before the Whitley Council's first meeting, student nurses, registered nurses, and male nurses assembled in Trafalgar Square and marched in procession to Hyde Park. There, one of the students courageously harangued her colleagues from a coal-cart. Press photographers were naturally active. On the following day it is not too much to say that the country was genuinely touched; these young girls, starting in a vital and in some ways selfless profession, were getting a raw deal. Something must be done about it.

The young nurses did it for themselves, however. The less militant-minded appealed for help to their local Members of Parliament, and, naturally, to the Student Nurses Association at the Royal College of Nursing, of which the young Princess Elizabeth, now the Queen, was President.

The College negotiators broached the matter at the first Whitley Council meeting which was held next day and, naturally, were backed by the other organizations.

But the Government had already appreciated the danger; the Management Side of the Council were conciliatory and agreed to consider demands. With surprising speed—the negotiations took less than two months, something like a record for any official committee—the student nurses received a rise of pay which more than compensated for the heavier insurance contribution.

The fact that the simpler way of dropping the contribution was not adopted is understandable. If the National Health Service was to gain the confidence of all, it must be compulsory that all, whether rich, poor, high, or low, should pay the contribution. Without this no Minister could have had a hope of defending the enormous additional cost to the taxpayer of the great river of free-prescription medicine which soon began pouring down the national throat. If, of course, student nurses had in fact been granted true student status, for which the College had fought so long, they would, like other students, not have been liable to pay National Insurance contributions. But this is a battle which is still to be won.

Thereafter the College delegates concentrated mainly on pressing for increases of pay for registered nurses and decreases of hours for all nursing staff. Now that the Government had made itself responsible for the whole organization, the Government must be forced to pay. There was nothing like the 'where-is-the-money-coming-from' blank wall that had held up such demands under the voluntary system.

In broad outline the National Health Service was to be administered through regional hospital boards, which controlled all hospitals other than teaching hospitals in England and Wales. Boards of Governors were appointed to each of the teaching hospitals, and acted directly under the aegis of the Minister of Health. The non-teaching hospitals were run by hospital management committees (acting under the larger direction of the regional hospital boards).

In general the working machinery of the N.H.S. showed itself to be of a practical design by which the vast reorganization of the medical and nursing professions could be nationally administered. Both doctors and nurses through their representative organizations had had their say in the planning. It seems probable, however, that the real issue—whether or not the nation could pay for an efficient service—had not been adequately considered. The country had only just emerged victorious from the most expensive war in history and—as after the First World War—found no practical possibility of collecting the just and rightful compensation owed to it.

It is, therefore, a tribute to the work of the College and other organizations on the Whitley Council that during the next nine years they got nurses five rises of pay in spite of the fact that the Government found itself forced to announce a wage freeze almost directly after the National Health Service was started. Governmental difficulties had been added to by the charge that the immense bill for the National Health Service was, in itself, a reason for general inflation. That these pay increases were granted was due to the fact that nurses' salaries had always been appallingly low and in 1948 were far below the general level.

Battles for pay rises to keep pace with the increases in cost of living have been constant across the Whitley Council table from that day to this. To give each demand and final concession in these pages would make very heavy reading, and in any case all the figures are available in the official reports. One or two will, perhaps, give a clear enough picture if a glance forward over the years covers some of the endless negotiations.

The College and the other Staff Side delegates on the Whitley Council in 1954 gave a detailed report on the cost-of-living rise since the increase granted two years earlier. They proved that the rise did not compensate for the increase in prices. Further, they were able to show the fall in value of salaries during the three years previous to 1952. They therefore asked for all grades to be granted compensation for half this fall in value, covering the three-year period, and also for a rise to meet the proved increase in cost of living since 1952.

There was tough negotiation across the table, but the Management would grant no more than £25 for staff nurses and £15 for students. This the Staff Side would not accept. They pointed out that this did not fully compensate for the cost-of-living rise since 1952, let alone the other claim. The Management Side flatly refused to consider the other claim, saying that any differentials before 1952 were irrelevant. This 'yes-it-is-no-it-isn't' argument ended in deadlock as such arguments usually do, and the Staff Side demanded that the question go to arbitration. Which was a pity since arbitration decided in favour of the Management Side!

However, such results are all in the luck of the game, and over the years the Staff Side has generally gained a good part of, and in many cases the full amount of its demands. One case of this was the principle advocated by the College for years, for equal pay for male and female nurses. As in so many other fields male nurses had within human memory always received more than female.

The asylum rate for men, according to the prevailing scales at any time, had not been much higher, but as men began to come into general hospital nursing, the fact that their pay was more than that of women of level grade naturally caused resentment. Both girls and men were doing the same work. Granted the men were physically stronger but they were not required to use this advantage either in types of work or length of hours. The old fighting spirit of the emancipation of women was still strong within the College, and the demand for equal pay was carried to the Whitley Council table where at first it met resistance.

However the Staff Side pressed the demand firmly, and pointed out that the Government had promised to introduce equal pay for men and women in the public services. What were nurses if they were not a public service? Were they not part and parcel of the National Health Service?

There was no way out. The Management Side had to agree. Equal pay was granted but, typically, in a number of stages spread over the next six years (from 1955). From this they would not be budged by any form of argument. Still, the battle was won, and the College could add another laurel to its ensign.

The battle of the hours at the Whitley Council meetings has kept pace with the pay question. The College was always to the fore in its demands for reduction and, it will be remembered, persuaded many of the voluntary hospitals to adopt a ninety-six-hour fortnight directly after the First World War. The cost of hours-reduction under either the voluntary or the national systems is of necessity high. Hospitals must provide a twenty-four-hour service seven days a week. Shorter hours mean more trained personnel working in shifts, who must be paid. The shortage of nurses which has persisted to this day adds an obvious complication.

Even so, by the persistent negotiations of the Staff Side, the Management Side of the Whitley Council has gradually made concessions over the years. The result is that hospitals generally as from 1 January 1966 are working an eighty-four-hour fortnight, and student nurses have far more time for study and lectures. In addition a generous superannuation scheme has been introduced, and living conditions, general amenities, and now the prospect of overtime payments are beyond anything of which the 1900 nurse could have dreamed.

A smaller but quite considerable item is that the uniform which the voluntary-hospital nurse had to pay for herself, is now provided free under the N.H.S. In addition the deductions for 'residence'—board and lodging—made to the salaries of staff living-in have been held below the general standard of cost of living.

This of course has made the living-in nurse financially better off than her living-out colleague, but only to the extent that would be experienced by a clever manager of money.

For the single girl, living out, alone, has its drawbacks; there is a very real companionship and social life in any well-run hospital and the old, restrictive idiocies of the 'lights-out-at-ten' variety have entirely disappeared.

CHAPTER TWENTY-SIX

Nurses Act 1949

In 1948 from the professional point of view the thunder and the shouting over the N.H.S. had died and the captains and the kings had departed . . . to get on with the job and try and make the newly implemented service work. The rank and file —if the lay public may so be referred to—took up the cries of battle, as is their usual habit, when matters had gone too far for quick or easy alteration to be possible.

Despite the fact that national responsibility for health and welfare had been an all-party concept, the new service was vilified as wild, impractical Socialistic ideology. It was said that doctors in general practice no longer bothered themselves with anything that couldn't be dealt with by pot., brom., or a dose of salts, but were merely ticket signers for hospital reception. It was shown that individuals of our (then) tiny coloured population were getting prescriptions for straightening the curls in their hair, and that medicaments costing a guinea a dose were being showered, free, upon the public at large. The Royal College of Nursing came in for some of the general obloquy because it had made no secret of the fact that it had worked hard to help shape and implement the service.

Of course, doctors being human creatures, there were some who prescribed irresponsibly in regard to cost. The hospitals became overloaded, with the result that many genuine sufferers found themselves having to wait long periods for admission. Things reached the state that hospitals had to limit new admissions to cases of immediate urgency. Every case of anomaly or difficulty received a thousand times the acreage of publicity it would normally have merited. The comic papers and the comedians were in their element, and indeed some of the jokes were very much to the point.

In a film made at the time the late Basil Radford was to be

11

seen telephoning doctor after doctor, and appearing at the doors of various out-patient departments, complaining gently but pathetically about his lumbago—without getting attention anywhere. Later in the film's movement he appeared, supine upon a stretcher, being carried into a hospital. But, catching sight of an acquaintance, he sat up, waving and shouting: 'Hello old boy. Just had a bit of luck! Fell over and broke my leg!'

In short, like any new and untried system, the National Health Act was infinitely more criticized for its failures than its successes. But from the start its basic success was assured for without it, or a measure very much like it, the voluntary-hospital system had been bound to collapse owing to the combined forces of rising costs and rising population.

However, at first it seemed that nurses were to be the Cinderellas of the Act. Neither the central Government nor the local authorities appeared to realize that while care of the sick may be regarded as the architecture of the system, nursing is the keystone without which it could not exist.

The setting up of a Standing Nursing Advisory Committee of the Central Health Services Council by the Ministry, to advise the Minister on nursing matters, was announced in 1948. The proposed composition indicated that nurses would be much in the minority of the membership, a situation that, today, would be regarded as idiotic. Whether Mr. Bevan thought that only those at the very top of the nursing organizations were capable of acting with common sense is not recorded, but vigorous efforts on the part of the College helped to achieve a nurse majority. Much the same sort of thing was going on throughout the whole structure of the service. Mr. Bevan had made his nurse appointments to the regional hospital boards, but most of the hospital management committees (which were closest to all nursing problems) were without nurse or adequate nursing-representation membership. The College, naturally, pressed for matrons to be, even if *ex officio*, upon hospital management committees.

Meanwhile, since it was natural enough that details and complexities of the new service were not well known even to the qualified and experienced, the College started a series of meetings of nurses who had been appointed to the regional hospital boards or management committees. At these meetings all problems of staffing hospitals and running efficient nursing services within the new regulations were gone into in detail. Further, all who attended were brought up to date on the progress of negotiations for the revision of nurses salaries. This enabled them to speak with authority not only in their board work but in dealing with hospital staff, and proved to be a strong factor in removing misunderstandings and nullifying uninformed criticism.

Towards the end of the year a new Nurses Bill (to become the Nurses Act, 1949, amending the Nurses Acts of 1919 and 1943) was in its final stages of drafting, in which the College, by invitation of the Ministry of Health, had been active with proposals and advice. The Bill which was confined to England and Wales reconstituted the General Nursing Council. A further object was to separate the finances of nurse training from the budgets of hospitals, as far as was practicable, and to allow for experimentation in nurse training which had not previously been possible.

Nurse-training committees were to be set up for regional hospital board areas to help the General Nursing Council and training institutions by improving nurse training methods. Funds for approved experimental nursing schemes were to be provided through the General Nursing Council and nurse-training committees instead of through hospital boards and boards of Governors.

There were clauses of the Bill providing for a new mental nurses committee within the General Nursing Council. Admission to the Register of nurses trained abroad (by individual cases) was proposed together with the inclusion of male nurses on the general part of the Register. Machinery was detailed for appeal against withdrawal of the Council's approval of a training institution, and publication of the Register was in future to be periodic rather than annual. There was also a mass of minutiae concerning financial matters in general.

The College was satisfied with this clean-sweeping measure which it had very largely helped to frame, and at once circulated details to the branches. The reaction of the whole nursing profession was one of praise for work well done. However, as might have been expected, there was heated opposition from some parts of the medical profession and from hospital administrators—they did not like the nurse-training schools to be out of their direction.

This opposition was powerful and vocal. The College knew it and wasted no time in launching counter-attacks. A letter was sent to thirty-two members of the House of Lords in which independence for the nurse-training committees was shown to be vital if the profession was to progress and not stay bogged down where it had been for years. The letter asked also that the following points should be insisted upon:

(1). That the nurse-training committees should be renamed 'Councils'. Not quite such a trivial matter as it might appear. By changing the title in this way, any idea that they were under the jurisdiction of the regional hospital boards would be removed.

(2). That experienced administrators of educational funds should be recruited to these training councils.

(3). That steps be taken to safeguard the quality of training schemes as they were developed.

(4). That nurses with wider experience of nursing education be included on the General Nursing Council.

(5). That boards of Governors of the great teaching hospitals (which retained a much greater freedom under the N.H.S.) be required to submit to the General Nursing Council estimates for nurse training.

The Nurses Bill, 1949 was sponsored by the Minister of Health and introduced into the House of Lords in April. There were the expected battles in the committee stage, some points lost, some gained. The great wrangle came over the financial control of nurse-training budgets, as the College had foreseen. However, their supporters carried the day before the report stage. The area nurse training committees were confirmed in their financial powers. A new clause set up a Statutory Finance Committee within the General Nursing Council vested with special powers, and there were to be three added members appointed by the Minister, who were to be well versed in hospital administration.

If rather full space has been devoted to this Bill it is because, basically, it was the measure most historically important in the development of the nursing profession that had been framed since the original Nurses Registration Act in 1919.

After the first reading in the House of Commons, College representatives were invited to an interested non-party meeting of M.P.s at the House to stress the special points still at issue. On second reading the Opposition offered no amendments of substance. The discussions at the report stage were chiefly upon which expenses should be devoted to administration, and which to nurse training.

The College's justifiable criticism, that the proposed Finance Committee of the General Nursing Council was not, by its constitution, required to appoint people who knew anything about finance, was met. A Government motion empowered the addition of two persons, not being General Nursing Council members, but who were experienced in the administration of educational funds, to the Council's Finance Committee. The new General Nursing Council was constituted of seventeen elected and seventeen appointed members. Fourteen of the elected were to be nurses, both male and female, on the General Part of the Register, two were to be registered mental nurses (one male and one female), and one a registered sick children's nurse.

Of the appointed members twelve were to be nominated by the Ministry of Health, three by the Ministry of Education, and two by the Privy Council (one representing English and Welsh universities). The Ministry of Health appointments were to include two public-health nurses, two sister tutors, one male nurse, one ward sister, and three people experienced in hospital management.

When, on 25 November, the Nurses Act, 1949 received the Royal Assent, the College could congratulate itself upon having virtually influenced the framing of a measure which assured the profession of a future of improving conditions.

CHAPTER TWENTY-SEVEN

Post-War Problems

THE THIRD General Secretary, Catherine Mary Hall, took over the reins from Frances Goodall on 1 June 1957. A Yorkshire woman, she had spent the greater part of her life and gained most of her professional experience in the north of England, and was the first General Secretary who had received her nursing training in a provincial hospital.

In 1941 she entered the School of Nursing at the General Infirmary, Leeds, and spent the majority of the next fourteen years at that hospital. It was while she was Night Superintendent that Catherine Hall had the opportunity to study abroad. She was awarded the first fellowship offered by the Board of Governors of the United Leeds Hospitals to nurses in one of the Board's hospitals. At the end of 1950 she left Leeds to spend six months studying administration and teaching in hospitals and university schools of nursing in America and Canada.

She returned home in 1951 and went back to the General Infirmary at Leeds and shortly afterwards was appointed Assistant Matron. In the autumn of 1953 Catherine Hall became a student at the Royal College of Nursing in the Nursing Administration (Hospital) Course and at the end of the following year was appointed Assistant Matron at the Middlesex Hospital, London.

Some two years later she was appointed General Secretary Designate at the Royal College of Nursing and after a year in this office became General Secretary. She has at the time of writing held this post for nine years—six with the Royal College of Nursing and three (since 1963) with the amalgamated Royal College of Nursing and National Council of Nurses.

The three General Secretaries of the College have each concentrated on developments reflecting the needs of their

eras. Mary Rundle undertook the task of building the College
into a truly representative body of the nursing profession.
Francis Goodall concentrated on forcing recognition of the
College at Governmental level in all matters pertaining to the
needs of nurses and patients. Since Catherine Hall became
Secretary, concentration has been increasingly on decentraliza-
tion and greater membership participation.

No mention of the three General Secretaries would be
complete without including a reference to Jean Page who
joined the staff of the College in 1932 as Personal Secretary
to Mary Rundle, continued in this position with Frances
Goodall, and subsequently became Personal Assistant to the
General Secretary when Catherine Hall was appointed. One
of her duties has always been to attend Council meetings and
to 'service' the Honorary Officers. She has seen the membership
more than double its number and has known all the 'giants' of
the College, as she calls them, including Dame Sarah Swift and
Sir Arthur Stanley.

The College has always been concerned with the problem
of communications and the importance of giving members the
opportunity to play an active part in the advancement of the
profession and nursing service. Through the development of
the branches and the establishment of new sections as the need
arose a ready means of communication was provided—in
1949 the Ward and Departmental Sisters Section, which had
previously been a self-supporting group, in 1953 the Occupational Health Section whose members had previously been
a part of the Public Health Section, and in 1960 a Nurse
Administrators group which became a full section the following
year.

The institution of 'key' members in hospitals and other
places where nurses worked was another means of bringing the
College to the membership. Kept constantly informed of
activities through news sheets the key member is a ready source
of information about the College. At the same time more
publicity for the meetings of the national delegate body
resulted in lively debate on the resolutions put forward by the
branches. The establishment of area offices with full time
secretarial help for the area organizers was another major

step forward in strengthening contact with the membership while area conferences became a regular feature.

The College early recognized that while a unified policy was necessary, the different countries that make up the United Kingdom had their own particular problems and, in the case of Scotland and Northern Ireland, separate legislation. It was for this reason that national boards were established over the years. The first to be set up (in 1916) was the Scottish Board which quickly established itself as the body to be consulted on all nursing matters. Starting in one room in Edinburgh, it now has as its headquarters two adjoining houses in Heriot Row and an extensive educational and professional programme.

In 1943 the Committee for Northern Ireland was set up in Belfast. Like Scotland it rapidly expanded its professional and educational activities and now has permanent head-quarters at Windsor Avenue and the title Northern Ireland Board.

The Welsh Board was the last to be established. Largely as a result of the enthusiasm of the Welsh nurses themselves who in the first instance raised a large sum, the Board was set up in 1963. Later they actively supported the Appeal throughout the Principality which was organized by a special Appeal Committee of leading personalities in Wales. This resulted in the establishment of the beautiful new Headquarters, Ty Maeth, which was opened by Her Royal Highness, Princess Margaret Countess of Snowdon, in 1965.

In the years following the introduction of the Health Service an immense variety of problems arose, many of which were considered by Government committees and other official bodies. The College was constantly invited to submit memoranda of evidence on subjects ranging from general practice under the N.H.S., the provision of pharmaceutical services in hospital, the internal administration of hospitals, running costs of hospitals, drug addiction, the welfare of children in hospital, to hospital laundry arrangements. These resulted in recommendations to Government Departments and the statutory bodies and the issue of many reports on pro-fessional or educational matters affecting the nursing service;

others dealt with some immediate nursing problems such as the legal position of the nurse who, owing to the increasing pressure on the hospital service, was being required to undertake complex procedures normally regarded as being outside her professional duties; or the protection of nurses exposed to ionizing radiation.

The vexed question of the duties which the nurse should properly undertake became the subject of prolonged consideration and protracted discussion with the medical profession. Eventually in 1961 the College and the British Medical Association issued a joint document under the title 'The Duties and Position of the Nurse' setting out a procedure to be followed and the safeguards for nurses undertaking techniques outside the scope of their normal routine. This document, the first to be issued jointly with the medical profession, was followed by the publication of two joint memoranda with the Medical Defence Union—the first later that year and the second two years later—on safety measures which should be taken in hospital to minimize the making of avoidable errors in surgical operations. A colour film for teaching purposes, 'Make no Mistake', was subsequently produced jointly by the two bodies, based on these documents.

The College also initiated a series of conferences at which doctors, nurses, administrators, and members of hospital and local health authorities discussed together current problems. Starting in a small way these conferences have grown in size and importance and are now recognized as providing an unequalled opportunity for all those concerned with the Health Services to consider together major problems and their possible solution, to take account of new thought or fresh developments, and to introduce new ideas and experimental methods. A particularly interesting example of the initiative taken by the College in this way was the conference it organized in 1957 on Work Study and the Hospital Service. The interest and enthusiasm of those who attended and the welcome given to the suggestion that work study might help to solve some of the difficulties facing the hospitals was one of the outstanding features of this conference.

With the passing of the Mental Health Act in 1959, which

aroused widespread interest in the needs of the mentally ill and in methods of treatment and was generally welcomed as a major advance in the social progress of the country, the College provided an opportunity of considering the implications of the Act at a conference entitled 'Mental Health—Today and Tomorrow', which was attended by some 700 doctors, nurses, and others concerned with the care of the mentally ill.

The increasing difficulty of obtaining adequate numbers of nursing staff for night duty in hospitals led the Council of the College to set up a working party to look into the question. The resulting Report issued by the College—'The Problem of Providing a Continuous Nursing Service Especially in Relation to Night Duty'—showed that a great part of the difficulty (apart from the perennial nurse shortage) was due to unsatisfactory conditions on night duty, and an understandable reluctance in many cases to undertake this part of the total nursing duty necessary to provide a twenty-four-hour service.

Shorter periods of night duty were recommended, with more adequate arrangements for nights off. On average the Report found that ward night staff were expected to do far too much work during the early morning, and felt a compulsive strain to complete the schedule. This brought about a deterioration in nursing standards, such as arousing patients at 5 a.m.

The Report made detailed recommendations concerning the trained nurse on night duty, students and pupil nurses on night duty, and reviewed the pattern of patient care from the traditional view and from the changing circumstances to be expected in the future. It emphasized that what many hospitals needed was not more nurses but more and better auxiliaries, domestics, and orderlies. In far too many instances trained and student nurses were still burdened with non-nursing duties.

This Report of the College was taken into consideration and many of its recommendations incorporated in a report subsequently issued by the Standing Nursing Advisory Committee on the Pattern of the In-Patient's Day. In view of the wide interest which these two reports had aroused, the College arranged one of its most stimulating conferences, 'The Hospital

Patient—Person or Case?', which attracted an audience of over 500. The Conference, in trying to determine what the patient in hospital really needed and what changes might be made in the interests of the patient, was marked throughout by the awareness of the importance of human relationships.

CHAPTER TWENTY-EIGHT

Opening the Doors

EARLIER CHAPTERS have made it clear that at the time the College of Nursing was founded there was no uniform standard of training for nurses. The College therefore determined its criteria for membership on a recognized training in 'general nursing' which it regarded as the basic professional preparation. It was taken for granted that the members should be women; indeed at that time men in general nursing were the exception if they were to be found at all, so any question of their non-acceptance by the College did not arise.

The Nurses Act of 1919 which gave statutory recognition to those who met the requirements laid down, provided for a General Register—open to women nurses only—and Supplementary Registers for men, for those who had trained in the nursing of the mentally sick or of the mentally subnormal, for those trained in the nursing of sick children, and of fevers. However as the years passed all branches of nursing became very highly specialized; the theoretical content of each course became more complex; more men entered nursing and undertook general training, and there was growing recognition of the contribution they had to make.

In due course this led to changes in legislation; the supplementary part of the register for male nurses who had taken a general training was merged into the General Register by the Nurses Act, 1949, but men were still not eligible for membership of the College.

This position could only be changed by amendments to the Royal Charter but in 1949 the College membership was not yet ready for this change. Still the Supplementary Registers remained for specialist training, but those who advocated specialization were satisfied that the professional content of these trainings was no less demanding than that of general training. Therefore existing legislation was amended, this time in favour of the specialists. The Nurses Act of 1957 did away with the General Register and the Supplementary Registers and substituted one Register with various parts—the general part and parts for nurses trained as specialists in various fields.

The College still admitted only the general trained woman nurse but this was not to continue for much longer. There had been some simmering within the membership on this issue for several years, and this began to make itself felt to a much greater extent. Some members started to campaign actively for the admission to the College of men who had undertaken a general training; further, members working in the psychiatric field were incensed that those who had undertaken a training in this type of nursing were excluded from College membership. Resolutions from branches came up to the Branches Standing Committee urging that College membership be extended with the result that in 1959 a Resolution was carried and referred to the Council for action.

Immediately the Council set up a Working Party under the Chairmanship of Miss Florence Udell, then Nurse Hon. Treasurer and later President of the College,* to consider the implications of the extension of membership. In time the Working Party recommended to the Council in favour of amending the Charter to permit all individuals whose names appeared on the register of a statutory nursing body in the United Kingdom to join the College.

The first hurdle was thus passed, it now remained to be seen if the members were ready to support this fundamental change in the original concept of the College.

At an Extraordinary General Meeting in June 1960 the decision was taken: it was overwhelmingly in favour of the Working Party's recommendation, all members of the College having had the opportunity of recording their views by postal ballot. So thereafter Her Majesty the Queen in Council was petitioned to allow the necessary amendment to the Royal Charter. This was granted and on 1 November 1960 the change became operative.

* See p. 170.

Prior to that date application had been received from those who had previously been ineligible for membership, particularly from men, several of whom had the ambition to be the first male nurse to be enrolled as a member of the College. It was therefore fitting that one man who had for many years campaigned for this extension of College membership should become, immediately this change became effective, the first male nurse to be appointed to the staff of the College. The fact that he was also a trained mental nurse with considerable experience in the psychiatric field enhanced the contribution which he has since been able to make. Since then a number of men (not all nurses) have been appointed to the staff.

The change in the extension of College membership was highly significant for the future role of the College. The following year the Nurses (Amendment) Act, 1961 was passed. By the provisions of this Act enrolled nurses dropped the title they had hitherto borne of 'assistant' and the Assistant Nurses Committee of the General Nursing Council for England and Wales became henceforth the Enrolled Nurses Committee. Similar legislation was passed for Scotland and Northern Ireland.

The College was now emerging as the body with the responsibility to represent all registered nurses—embracing those engaged in all fields of nursing work, irrespective of sex.

CHAPTER TWENTY-NINE

The Royal College and
the National Council—Amalgamation

THIS CLEARED the way for the next step, which many had seen as desirable for a number of years but had doubted could be brought to achievement, namely, the coming together of the National Council of Nurses of Great Britain and Northern Ireland and the Royal College of Nursing.

Within a few years of its foundation in 1916 the College with its active policy had become the recognized voice of professional nursing in the country. It was the body which spoke and acted on behalf of registered nurses at national level.

This, however, did not apply in the international sphere in which another organization, the National Council of Nurses of Great Britain and Northern Ireland officially represented the nursing profession of the United Kingdom. This situation was the result of historical development.

Reference has already been made to the International Council of Nurses founded in 1900 by Ethel Bedford Fenwick, which was the first international organization for *professional* women. Its Constitution laid down that only one nursing organization from each country might be in membership, and that such an organization must be composed exclusively of nurses. When the I.C.N. was established there was no organization in the United Kingdom which met the requirements for membership. Mrs. Bedford Fenwick had therefore founded one —the National Council of Nurses.

This was constituted as a federation. From the outset member bodies included not only associations of trained nurses but also the Nurses Leagues of hospitals many of whose members were married or retired.

In 1925 the College of Nursing discussed with the International Council the possibility of the College being recognized as the representative body of the United Kingdom. The rules of the International Council however did not permit it, once it had accepted one body as the national nursing organization of a country, to accept another organization in its place.

Had the members of the College of Nursing at that time decided to force the issue to its logical conclusion, the outcome can only be surmised. The College accepted the decision but decided that in order to influence nursing policy at international level it must apply for membership of the National Council which was the representative body for the United Kingdom on the International Council. The application was made and accepted that year.

In order to avoid the College of Nursing by its great membership dominating the National Council a system was drawn up which limited the representation of the College although dues were levied on the total membership.

(The National Council also accepted into full membership organizations representing nurses then not eligible for membership of the College—male nurses, psychiatric nurses, sick children's nurses. This, as has been recorded, was adjusted in 1960 when the College decided in favour of extending membership.)

Throughout the years this question of 'no taxation without representation' was a matter of dispute between the College and the National Council, particularly as the College was not infrequently the only member body of the National Council which had the facilities and the knowledge to undertake surveys, prepare reports, or complete questionnaires for the International Council. Moreover, as has been said, a significant section of the voting power lay with nurses out of touch with the latest needs and problems of the profession. When war broke out in 1939 the National Council suspended activities. The College, however, undertook on its behalf the limited international activities which the war years imposed.

In the immediate post-war years when the National Council resumed its activities, duplication of work and effort resulted from the existence of the National Council and the College as separate bodies. The position detracted from the image of

British nursing at international level and from the part which British nurses could play in world nursing affairs.

In short, the College, the body which was most concerned with formulating nursing policy at national level—which was recognized as the voice of professional nursing at home—was not the one with the right to speak at international level.

It was realized that the greatest difficulty to be overcome was the background of antipathy between the two organizations; this had not been entirely lost over the years. Ethel Bedford Fenwick's influence was still potent. Even so, the two bodies had learned to live together but the process of actually coming together, of merging into one organization, was a slow and painful one. There were prime movers both within the National Council and the College—those who saw that, in the interests of the profession, a solution must be found and were prepared to plan, to work, and to try to convince others of the need.

One who had been convinced that the two bodies must be brought together, if the best interests of the profession were to be served, was Mabel Lawson. In 1957 she had been elected President of the National Council. She was a woman of wide experience and interests with a unique background since as far as is known she is the only woman to have qualified as a doctor and later given up medical practice to retrain and practise as a nurse.

Mabel Lawson had originally wanted to be a nurse, but her family had a medical background so she was told that she must take medical degrees. This she did at Aberdeen University and graduated in Arts for good measure. Then for the next nine years she practised in various corners of the kingdom from the Highlands to Somerset.

But she still wanted to be a nurse, so at last she came to London and trained at the Nightingale Training School at St. Thomas's Hospital. Later the London County Council appointed her Supervisor of Nurse Training Schools and in 1941 she was appointed Assistant to the Chief Nursing Officer at the Ministry of Health. Subsequently she was appointed Deputy Chief Nursing Officer, a post she held until her retirement in 1957.

12

When the war ended Mabel Lawson went to occupied Germany with the Control Commission to help re-establish the national nursing service.

When the amalgamation with the Royal College of Nursing was first mooted on the National Council, she pointed out that since 1947 a sense of confusion regarding international relationships and a lack of unity at home had resulted in a weakness in the Council's affairs detrimental to its standing both at home and abroad. This had been felt acutely by British nurses at the International Congress in Rome in 1957.

The whole structure of the National Council for these obvious reasons was in vital need of overhaul. Things had altered vastly during the sixty years of its life, but the constitution of the organization had altered little although many suggestions for modernizing its structure had been put forward over the years.

In 1959 the National Council established a Constitution Standing Committee to consider how best British nurses might be organized. As a result of these discussions a proposal that there should be a united professional body based on individual membership was approved by the majority of member bodies of the National Council at an Extraordinary Grand Council Meeting the following year. The meeting agreed that the Constitution Standing Committee should negotiate direct with the College with a view to drawing up a detailed plan for implementation of the proposal.

The broad issue of amalgamation was won. All that remained were the careful detailed negotiations skilfully carried out by the representatives appointed by the two bodies.

The year 1962 saw the culmination of many years of negotiation. In February the Grand Council of the National Council of Nurses approved proposals for a unified body to be achieved by the amalgamation of the National Council and the College. By agreement between the two bodies, the proposals were based on the Royal Charter of the College. The necessary amendments to the Charter to give effect to the amalgamation were finally approved at an Extraordinary General Meeting of the College in June. As the amendments were so extensive the College petitioned Her Majesty the Queen for the grant of a Supplemental Charter which was received in May 1963.

The two bodies were thus officially amalgamated under the title of 'The Royal College of Nursing and National Council of Nurses of the United Kingdom'. The rather cumbersome title has been reduced in its outline to 'Rcn' in which it will be clear that 'College of Nursing' and 'Council of Nurses' are both expressed in equal degree, in the lower case 'cn' which follows the capital 'R' for Royal.

The amalgamated body was doubly honoured when Her Majesty the Queen, who had been Patron of the Royal College since the death of its first Patron Queen Mary in 1953, and Queen Elizabeth the Queen Mother who had been Patron of the National Council, both consented to become Patrons of the joint organization. At St. James's Palace in June, to mark the amalgamation, the Queen Mother presented the magnificent new Chain of Office of the amalgamated body, made possible by very generous gifts from a number of members. The new Chain, which is of 18-carat gold, incorporates in its links the four national emblems; the centre link is a moonstone, symbolic of nursing, surrounded by diamonds and sapphires, and the pendant a reproduction of the coat of arms in gold and enamel.

The *Nursing Times* described the new situation:

'The Royal College of Nursing now speaks not only nationally for its members . . . but for every British nurse at international level. In other words if you are a member of the Rcn you have representation both nationally and internationally but if you are a member of some other professional organization, while you may have some say in national affairs affecting your particular nursing group, as far as international matters are concerned, the say is said for you by the Rcn members who belong to an organization which is recognized internationally as the voice of the Registered Nurses of the United Kingdom. . . .

'It must be borne in mind that even if one is not a member of the Rcn, decisions will be made for one by colleagues within an organization composed exclusively of registered nurses, which is fully representative of all fields of nursing;

therefore these decisions are likely to be reasonable and based upon wide and varied views.

'The new amalgamated body has undoubtedly taken on a grave responsibility. As far as the world is concerned statements of the Rcn will represent what British nurses as a whole are thinking. . . .'

As perhaps the leading architect of the amalgamation, one who had not only had the vision but had also proved herself a skilled negotiator and successful conciliator able to make the vision a reality, it was fitting that Mabel Lawson should be elected the first President of the amalgamated body. This office she held for a year, a strenuous year for any President and a formative one in the history of the joint organization. At the end of that time she chose not to stand for re-election, instead she was unanimously elected Nurse Honorary Treasurer and as such continued, a greatly valued elder statesman of the organization.

Mabel Lawson was succeeded as President by Florence N. Udell. The election of Miss Udell was another significant act on the part of the Council of the amalgamated body. If Mabel Lawson had been a prime mover for amalgamation from the National Council side, then Florence Udell had to a great extent been her counterpart from within the inner circles of the College.

Florence Udell was elected to the Council of the College in 1950, and in 1959 she became Nurse Honorary Treasurer. For many years she had also been active in the work of the International Council of Nurses. It was a proud day for her when in 1964 she succeeded Mabel Lawson and became the second President of the organization she had so long desired to see. Incidentally there was another reason too—she was only the second former member of the College staff to become the President.

Florence Udell trained at the Radcliffe Infirmary, Oxford and became a member of the College of Nursing in 1925. She was appointed to the post of Secretary of the Public Health Section of the College in 1931. After further work in the field, the College appointed her Area Organizer for Scotland in 1937 and within a year she was appointed Secretary of the Scottish Board.

When the war became imminent she was responsible for the greater part of the organization of the Scottish Civil Nursing Reserve. Further, she served on the Nurses' Salaries Committee for Scotland (the Taylor Committee, the counterpart in Scotland of the Rushcliffe Committee) as one of the College representatives and was made Chairman of the Staff side. Towards the end of the war Miss Udell was appointed Chief Nurse in the Health Division of the European Regional Office of U.N.R.R.A., and on her return Chief Nursing Officer, Colonial Office, and later Nurse Adviser, Ministry of Overseas Development.

CHAPTER THIRTY

Salaries, Hours, and Overtime

ONCE THE College had amalgamated with the National Council of Nurses under the terms of the Supplemental Charter it might well have seemed that the joint body was now fully representative of the nursing profession at both national and international level. But whilst discussions and negotiations had been going on to achieve these changes the profession, itself, was developing; more and more emphasis was being placed on the contribution of the enrolled nurse. Great efforts were being made to attract the right type of recruits into this training. The Nurses (Amendment) Act, 1961 which deleted the word 'Assistant' from the title of the enrolled nurse was warmly welcomed as at last giving recognition to her important role in the nursing team. As far back as 1942 the Nursing Reconstruction Committee in its first Report had stated that the position of the enrolled nurse was pivotal in the interests of the service. In 1943 the National Association of State Enrolled Nurses had been founded; it became an affiliated body of the Royal College of Nursing which gave it support and assistance over the years. It is now a flourishing organization with a membership in the region of 4,000.

Another large group engaged in the nursing services of the country but not eligible for College membership are the student nurses. In 1925 the College set up within itself a Student Association but by 1949 the members of the Association voted to be an independent and autonomous body. A new constitution was therefore drawn up for the Association giving it independence but maintaining close relationship with the College: for instance, the College Council appointed representatives to serve on the governing body of the Association. This close relationship has continued. The officials of the two Associations work closely together, the College provides expert advice and services through its specialist representatives, but constitutionally the Association remains independent.

The pendulum, however, is now swinging back, because there is a growing body of opinion that the interests of the profession, and the students themselves, would be better served if the student body became an integral part of the professional organization of the Rcn.

The years that followed the inception of the National Health Service were years of consistently rising prices. Although the Staff Side of the Nurses and Midwives' Whitley Council was able to obtain improvements in salaries and conditions of service for nurses in the Health Service over the next decade, the struggle was long and arduous. It never succeeded in getting for nurses salaries and hours of work comparable with other professions owing to the very low level of salaries and long hours of work that obtained when the Health Service was established. From the beginning difficulties mounted.

In 1950 just as agreement on new salary scales for senior staff in general hospitals had been reached the Government issued its White Paper on Incomes. As a result the Management Side stated it was unable to start negotiations for revised scales for public health and domiciliary nurses. The Staff Side was successful in having the matter referred to arbitration and for the first time the Industrial Court heard a dispute regarding nurses' salaries. The award of the Court was that negotiations should commence immediately and subsequently the Staff Side was able to announce that new scales had been agreed. In succeeding years there were references to arbitration by the Industrial Court on the date of implementation of agreed revised salaries, on revised salaries for mental nurses and London weighting for non-resident staff. In all cases the Court awarded in favour of the Staff Side.

In spite of the improvements achieved as a result of hard negotiations, however, nurses' salaries at the beginning of the 'sixties still lagged behind other professions. The culmination came in 1961 when the Staff Side submitted a new claim. The proposals were designed to simplify the salary structure as well as to provide a substantial increase in the scales for each grade.

No agreement was reached but the following year the Management Side made an offer of an increase of 2½ per cent. This was rejected by the Staff Side and in the weeks that followed the College took a leading part in the campaign to arouse the interest and support of the general public in the efforts to obtain more adequate salaries for all nurses and midwives. In March the College called an emergency meeting in the Cowdray Hall—the number who came astounded the organizers. The building was veritably jammed with nurses who overflowed the hall and crowded the stairways and other floors to which the proceedings of the meeting were relayed by loud speakers.

At the meeting it was resolved that the Government must be put under pressure by protest meetings all over the country. When these were held they proved to be just as crowded and enthusiastic as the original one in the Cowdray Hall. Deputations to Members of Parliament were organized and the national Press, radio, and television gave publicity to the nurses' cause. The nurses, however, unanimously agreed at every meeting that the one weapon none of them would use—or even threaten to use—was that of the strike.

While that was going on the College was inundated with telephone calls and letters of encouragement from the non-nursing general public throughout the country, most asking how help could be given. The College briskly followed up what was showing itself to be a wave of genuine national feeling and circulated every single Member of Parliament.

At the same time the Staff Side set up a Special Committee to co-ordinate activities, arranged deputations to all three parliamentary political parties, and organized a mass meeting at the Albert Hall in London which was attended by over seven thousand nurses, many Members of Parliament, and representatives of interested organizations. The chair was taken by Jo Grimond, Leader of the Liberal Party, and the speakers were Dame Irene Ward, Conservative, and Kenneth Robinson, Labour, in addition to the Secretary of the Staff side.

Following two Parliamentary debates on the salary position, negotiations were resumed but again broke down; the claim

The Royal Charter

The Presidential insignia is a finely-wrought chain with a jewelled centre link and pendant. It was made in 1963, the cost being met by a number of generous people all of whom have wished to remain anonymous.

The chain is 36 inches long and made of 18-carat gold containing links in the form of national emblems; the rose of England, the thistle of Scotland, the shamrock of Ireland, and the daffodil of Wales are placed on either side of the central link.

This central link is set with a moonstone—the stone which is the emblem of nursing—surrounded by twelve diamonds and twelve sapphires. On the rim, which is of blue enamel, is engraved the title of the organisation.

At the top of the pendant, below the centre link, an ornamental scroll carries the word 'PRESIDENT'. On the body of the pendant are the armorial bearings of the Rcn which were granted by the Kings of Arms with the Royal Authority vested in them and by warrant from the Earl Marshal.

On the Norman shield, the sun and stars denote day and night service. Above the shield is a casque, and a Roman lamp (symbolic of nursing) is imposed upon the book of learning.

The motto inscribed at the base is *Tradimus Lampada*— 'We hand on the Torch'.

The Grant of Arms

was then referred to the Industrial Court for arbitration. The Court awarded an immediate increase of 7½ per cent, together with a direction that negotiations be resumed on adjustments in the salary structure and on board-and-lodging charges. The resumed negotiations, however, broke down, and the questions were referred back to the Industrial Court which was asked to determine specimen salary scales for a number of grades upon which the remaining scales might be based. Following an award by the Court an agreement was finally reached.

When the questions of revised salary scales and an amended salary structure were before the Industrial Court, the Management Side had put forward a proposal for the introduction of a special payment of £1 per week to staff below the grade of ward sister for night duty and Sunday duty. The College representatives with the full support of the Staff Side tried repeatedly to persuade the Management Side to convert the proposed payments into increases in basic salary scales but without success. After prolonged negotiation special duty payments were finally accepted and introduced in 1963. The Rcn then sought the views of its branches on extension of these payments to other grades; the majority view was that there should rather be an improvement in basic salaries.

Although salaries and conditions had gradually been improved, there were still many salary anomalies, and nurses in 1963 were still working an eighty-eight-hour fortnight. A claim for a reduction to thirty-nine hours a week was unsuccessful, and eventually the Staff Side had to be satisfied with an agreement that hospital authorities should endeavour to reduce the hours of duty to eighty-four per fortnight as soon as possible and not later than December 1965.

This question of the number of hours nurses were expected to work had been, it will be remembered, a matter of concern to the College from the very beginning. Nurses themselves had been greatly exercised over this vexed question. With the perennial shortage of trained nurses, there was the problem of maintaining a twenty-four-hour service to the patient. As hours were gradually reduced over the years the question of payment for hours worked in excess of the standard working week had from time to time been raised. In 1963 the branches of the College through the Branches Standing Committee expressed the view that such payments were totally unsuitable as a method of remuneration for nurses and the College should continue to press for further improvement in the general level of salaries.

In the latter months of 1965 the Council of the Rcn had reason to re-examine the traditional policy of the College towards overtime payment for nurses. The principle followed by the Council had been to work for a reduction in basic hours and an increase in salaries, so that in order to 'see the job through' nurses would be treated as fairly as other professional groups.

Great changes in modern conditions with the general shorter working week, however, made this re-examination necessary. Although traditionally all grades in psychiatric hospitals (up to ward sister/charge nurse) had received overtime payments after the reduction of basic hours to eighty-eight per fortnight in 1962, overtime payments had been progressively reduced to payments to students and nursing assistants only. The effect of this, and with the enrolment of so many nursing assistants, was that most overtime was worked by student nurses.

The substantial proportion of part-time nurses employed in the Health Service further highlighted the problem. Part-time nurses are as vital to the service as the full-time but they are paid at an hourly rate for all hours worked, even if these are in excess of the time for which they were engaged. Moreover, the part-time rates show that the pay of nurses still compares unfavourably with that of other occupations inside and outside the N.H.S. A shorter basic working week would, of course, improve the part-time rates and give strength to the case for payment for excess hours to full-timers. If this were granted it would, additionally, provide a much stronger incentive for qualified nurses who had left the service to return, and relieve the serious shortage of fully skilled personnel.

On previous occasions when members had been asked for their opinion on overtime payments the reply had been overwhelmingly against the suggestion, and the Council knew that there was still acute feeling on the issue. The Rcn

Council therefore decided to take a referendum on the matter.

The result of the 1965 referendum, however, showed a substantial vote in favour of such payments (74 per cent). The National Association of State Enrolled Nurses which is affiliated to the Rcn also conducted a referendum of its members on the subject which resulted in a comparable percentage in favour. In the light of these results it was decided to press for overtime payments for all grades from enrolled nurses to ward and departmental sisters and charge nurses, and a claim was subsequently submitted by the Staff Side of the Whitley Council. (The Rcn Council had decided that it was better to leave unchanged the position of student nurses in this respect but to press for their exclusion from excess hours of duty.)

The Management Side decided that this was a major issue which could not be negotiated until the end of the present agreed 'standstill period', 1 July 1967, but the Staff Side declined to be satisfied with this and asked for a deputation to be received by the Ministry of Health.

After special duty payments had been in operation for some time, anomalies, which the Rcn had foreseen as inevitable from the outset, began to cause dissatisfaction among the membership; for instance, an experienced staff nurse on night duty who received the special duty payment could earn as much as or more than a night sister who was not eligible for such payment. As a result the Rcn Council in 1965 decided to seek the views of the members of the Ward and Departmental Section on this issue. The result of the referendum was overwhelmingly in favour of extending the payments to the ward-sister/charge-nurse grade.

Accordingly representations were made to the Staff Side which submitted a claim to the Management Side. Again the Management Side ruled that this was a major issue and could not be negotiated before 1 July 1967.

Up to the time of this work going to Press, that is where both matters stand.

CHAPTER THIRTY-ONE

The Platt Report

THE NATIONAL HEALTH SERVICE in recent years has come under more dangerous fire than that of the comic artists and comedians who sniped at it in its early days. The public in general took all that as it came; any new governmental measure is always fair game for mockery. Now, however, fundamental faults have developed which are far too close for comfort to every individual who has serious need of medical treatment. There has been criticism in the Press and over the broadcast services about the standard of hospital service, and maternity and out-patient services. A lowered standard of patient care, the incidence of sepsis, cross-infection, and wrong treatment have all been publicly discussed. A sharp illustration of the fall in public confidence has been the formation of patients' associations.

Concerned at the situation in nursing the Council of the Royal College appointed a Working Party in 1959 to study the position in nursing administration and the shortage of suitable applicants. Late in 1961 a committee under the chairmanship of Sir Harry Platt, Bt., Ll.D., M.D., M.S., F.R.C.S., President of the International Federation of Surgical Colleges, was formed to consider nurse education and training in the light of developments and the part the nurse is called on to play in the various spheres of nursing service.

In 1964 the Committee on Nurse Education published its first Report under the title 'A Reform of Nursing Education'. The Report, having set out the case for reform, outlined a new scheme of training.

The Report drew attention to the fact that during recent years the number of auxiliaries employed in hospital has increased out of all proportion to the increase in trained or partly trained nursing personnel. Such a large proportion of unqualified workers cannot contribute to a high standard of nursing care. The pressure and complexity of hospital work has increased with every year and the number of out-patients has multiplied; nurses' hours of work have, quite rightly, been reduced and their holidays lengthened. Moreover, if the profession is to recruit competitively, hours must be still further reduced in future.

Social change in the last twenty years has been greater than any in preceding centuries. The general standard of living has risen, our teenagers were born into a Welfare State, most professions are now open to women, and women generally have a much greater expectation of early marriage.

This means that the years of continuous service, which the nurse under the present system is likely to give to the profession, are reduced.

The Report is highly controversial. The scheme of training proposed is 'revolutionary in character and would require amending legislation'. But the committee believes that the recommended changes are vitally necessary.

In the first instance the Report states that if the needs of the service are to be met a well-balanced nursing team is essential, consisting of state registered and enrolled nurses supported by a non-nursing grade. A new grade, the ward assistant, is suggested, to combine the existing grades of nursing auxiliary and ward orderly. This grade is designed for those who wish to serve the sick, but have neither the desire nor ability to take training as a nurse.

Under the scheme proposed in the Report, regional councils for nursing education, financed by Exchequer grants, would be set up to be responsible for the organization and administration of the scheme. Schools of nursing, independent of the hospital service, would provide courses of training for registration and enrolment. The nursing student, who would be financially independent of the hospital service, receiving an educational grant on the same basis as other students, would follow a two-year course in the school covering academic study and practical experience. It would be the responsibility of the school council to make arrangements with the hospital authorities in the area for the provision of a proper range of clinical experience for the student and with local health authorities for practical experience in community health. It was recognized by the committee that close co-operation between the teaching staff of the school and the matron and senior nursing staff of the hospitals involved in providing the practical clinical experience, which would be planned in accordance with the student's educational needs, was essential.

While the student would contribute to the nursing service, she would not form part of the basic nursing staff of the hospital. She would, however, be responsible to the matron, through the sister in charge, for work she undertook in the care of patients. At the end of the second year the student would sit for her final examination. The third year would be spent in practical work, under supervision, in the hospital. The student would become eligible for registration following a favourable assessment of this year's work.

The Report reproduces one of the main planks in the general policy of the Royal College of Nursing—that nursing is a suitable subject for study at university level, and that success already achieved with experimental courses makes the establishment of a degree course in nursing a factor in the future development of the profession.

The whole concept of nursing education as detailed in the Report has its culmination in the 'well-balanced nursing team, supported by non-nursing grades' which it is designed to provide for hospitals in the future. The make-up of the team would of course vary according to whether or not the hospital concerned was taking part in basic nursing education.

The general trained registered nurse should be the team leader, to organize, supervise, and direct. Advancement open to her should be from staff nurse to ward sister and thereafter either in the fields of teaching or higher administration.

The enrolled nurse should be trained to give basic nursing care of the same standard as the registered nurse, but her range of functions and degree of responsibility should be more limited. Even so, the enrolled nurse would form the largest trained group in the hospital, and would deal with the major part of routine patient care. The future before the enrolled nurse should, in suitable cases and with the requisite training, lead to the positions of staff nurse or sister in appropriate wards.

Pupil nurses throughout their training should take their place in the team, doing routine work under supervision while receiving practical instruction. The new grade of ward assistants would undertake all tasks not requiring nursing skills but which form part of the direct service to patients. The ward sister should have the support of ward clerks, lay workers, voluntary or part-time, and a properly supervised and trained staff to deal with the general domestic work.

The Report states the belief that the scheme could be brought into being in its entirety without undue delay, although a transitional period is visualized during which the present and new schemes should operate together while staffing patterns within the hospital nursing service were adjusted.

This Report aroused probably more controversy than any other that the Rcn has issued. Those concerned with the provision of 'a pair of hands' and the effect the proposals would have on the staffing of hospitals regarded it as theoretical and idealistic; the majority of nurses welcomed it with enthusiasm as the first step in a new era for the nursing profession.

The Report was presented to the members of the Rcn at the professional conference at the Annual Meeting in June 1964. During the autumn the subject was discussed throughout the country by meetings organized by local branches and in October over 800 people representing all the interests concerned attended a national conference in London to thrash out the implications of the Report. Conferences were also arranged in Edinburgh, Belfast, and Cardiff, and early the following year the Report was further discussed at regional conferences throughout the country.

The Minister of Health sought the views of hospital authorities and other interested bodies but, despite repeated requests to the Minister by the Rcn for discussions regarding implementation of the Report, at the time of going to Press final discussion is still awaited.

CHAPTER THIRTY-TWO

Replanning Nursing Service

THE SECOND Report issued by the Rcn in 1964, 'Administering
the Hospital Nursing Service', is the complement of the
'Platt' Report already outlined; the two studied together form
a complete and comprehensive replanning of the country's
nursing service in all its forms.

This second Report is a development of the study into
nursing administration undertaken by the Working Party
set up in 1959, when a survey to obtain factual information
had been carried out and an assessment of the position
made. The changing situation at that time called for further
consideration of the position and this Report is the result of all
these deliberations.

The Report puts forward an entirely new plan for the top
administration of hospitals, surveys the drawbacks to each
existing senior post, and suggests the remedy in each case
together with some grade alterations.

Under the present system the responsibilities of the matron
vary widely, partly according to the size of the hospital and
partly according to the policy of the board of governors or
hospital management committee concerned. She is always
liable to be called upon at any hour of the twenty-four; she is
in many cases ultimately responsible for domestic services,
linen supply, laundry, dietetics, radiography, and the training
schools. At present it is obvious that all holding the higher
hospital posts—the deputy matron, assistant matron, administrative sister, or night superintendent—are expected to put in
long and irregular hours as a matter of course; their very lives
are absorbed in the constant problems and pressures of their
occupation. Moreover, their work generally has little to do with
nursing but much to do with forms and returns, supplies,
domestic matters, and staff control. The ward sister, the obvious

'material' for the moulding of senior administrators, has accepted long hours and a low salary because in her lifetime these have been the only standard conditions of employment for any who wanted to care for the sick. She is generally not attracted by still longer hours and work which deprives her of her deepest professional satisfaction, the close nurse-patient relationship, and the sense of doing something genuinely worth while, however meagre the recompense.

It is, in any case, a waste of knowledge and skill if the ward sister can rise further in her profession only by giving up the work in which she has made herself expert. Precisely the same may be said of the tutor or the clinical instructor. In many cases at present the circumstances in which both have to work make their tasks almost impossible. A large number of qualified tutors leave the hospital service every year for other teaching positions, return to clinical work, or transfer to administration.

The conclusion is obvious. Hospital administration as it stands is tradition-ridden, out-of-date, uneconomic—and offers so little incentive for training for senior positions that an observer is in no way surprised at the lack of applicants.

The Report therefore suggests that for each group of hospitals there should be one top-level nursing administrator whose span of control would equate with that of the group secretary, and whose duties would be to advise the hospital management on nursing, to be responsible for the top-level administration of the nursing and midwifery services within the group, and to frame the group nursing policy.

At hospital level there should be a senior nurse administrator whose span of control would equate with the hospital secretary and who would be responsible for the day-to-day administration of the nursing service in the individual hospital.

A new post of 'Clinical Nursing Officer' is suggested who would be responsible for day-to-day administration of a particular clinical area or unit. She would be aware of the situation affecting patients within the unit and would always be available to the ward sisters for consultation. She would form a vital link between the clinical situation and the general administration. The suggestion is made because the emphasis

13

upon clinical specialization is increasing rapidly—together with the complexity and specialization of almost every hospital service—and arrangements must be made to deal with the situation.

The ward sister remains, under the new plan, the most important member of the nursing team in direct and regular contact with the patients. It is suggested, however, that she should be relieved of non-nursing tasks. Provision of meals should be undertaken by the hospital catering department, although it must remain in the ward sister's power to advise on appropriate meals in all cases.

With present hours of duty and holidays ward sisters are at present in the ward for not more than a quarter of the total time required for a twenty-four-hour, seven-days-a-week service. To plan for three or four ward sisters to each ward would be unrealistic, but it is obvious that the necessary coverage could be provided at unit level by a 'duty rota' of a clinical nursing officer with three assistants who would provide night duty at supervisory level and make the appointment of a night sister unnecessary. If this pattern was followed in all units of the hospital, one of the clinical nursing officers on night duty could undertake any general administrative matter that arose, thus obviating the need for a night superintendent.

It is pointed out that under the existing system only a small number of matrons and their deputies or assistants have taken any full-time course of preparation for their positions. They have, in most cases, reached their positions by gradual promotion within a rigid system over twenty years or so. This is a long and laborious method and it is obvious that the constant pressure of responsibility and work in hand have left such senior administrators little opportunity of taking advanced courses.

Under the proposed new scheme of advanced nursing education, preparation for the most senior positions in the service is one of escalation, starting with the ward sister who may, if she holds the specialist qualification appropriate to the unit, choose to take a course to become a clinical nursing officer or, by further training, a clinical instructor.

Alternatively she may take the course to qualify as nurse

tutor, or if she is attracted by administrative work it is suggested that she may be given preliminary experience in the office of the hospital nursing officer before taking the course in nursing administration.

After due experience the clinical nursing officer may take preparation for possible promotion to hospital nursing officer. This should at least extend over one academic year and it is proposed that the course should be at university diploma level.

Applicants for the top grade of group nursing officer should be considered from hospital nursing officers who have taken all the successive courses of training from state registration upwards, and who have had sufficient experience in each grade.

In addition to a memorandum of evidence, both the foregoing Reports were submitted by the College to the committee set up in July 1963 by the Minister of Health and the Secretary of State for Scotland under the chairmanship of Mr. Brian Salmon to advise on the senior nursing staff structure in the hospital service, the administrative functions of the respective grades, and the methods of preparing staff to occupy them.

The report of the 'Salmon Committee' issued at the time of writing (May 1966) reflects much the same line of thinking as the Rcn Report on nursing administration.

The Salmon Report is detailed and comprehensive and will need intensive study. In outline it recommends that a new grading structure should take the place of the existing 'pyramid' structure in the hospital service in order to provide additional and different ways of advancement in administration, specialized nursing, and teaching. This is part of the movement away from the rigid and authoritarian system of command that has survived from the nineteenth century. It makes recommendations on preparation and selection for administrations, and suggestions for implementation. The report emphasizes that its findings are for the purpose of raising the status of nurses, ensuring their right to be heard on nursing matters, improving management, and benefiting patients.

'The Patient, himself,' says the Report, 'should be seen as fighting in the front line of the battle against illness, with the nursing, medical, and other staff together, providing the forward support, the intelligence and weapons, and the supplies.'

In 1964 a Working Party of the Rcn Occupational Health Section prepared a comprehensive memorandum of measures that should be taken to safeguard the health of all students and staff in the hospital service on lines similar to those provided in many industrial and commercial establishments. This was sent to the Minister of Health—and subsequently published— and a deputation also went to the Ministry to discuss the proposals in detail. The Minister of Health decided to set up a committee to consider the matter and, at the time of writing that committee is still sitting.

The memorandum refers to the International Labour Organization/World Health Organization Joint Committee Report on Occupational Health which agreed in 1950 that 'Occupational Health aims at the promotion and maintenance of the highest degree of physical, mental, and social well-being of workers in all occupations and the adaptation of work to man of each man to his job'.

The Report draws attention to the fact that, until recently, hospitals have only considered it necessary to provide emergency, treatment for students and staff becoming ill or injured at work, and little thought has been given to the positive approach to the health of all hospital workers. A hospital occupational health service would ensure the promotion of health and good working environment similar to those provided for many employees in industry and commerce.

Such a service would be complementary to the National Health Service.

In hospitals which have already established some form of health programme for nursing and other staff, the objective would be to widen the scope of such a programme and provide a comprehensive occupational health service for all hospital students and employees. In the planning or reorganization of hospitals it is important that consideration should be given to the provision of such a service, and at the planning stage the guidance of medical and nursing advisers from the occupational health field should be sought. It is of the utmost importance that, before the service is introduced and at each stage of development, consultation should take place between the employing authority and the employees.

The functions of a hospital occupational health service should be: pre-employment medical examination; routine follow-up examinations of, for example, workers exposed to special risks such as ionizing radiations, and after illness or accident; routine laboratory and X-ray investigations; immunization; to ensure that, by consultation with appropriate officers, the environment and working conditions in all places of employment within the hospital are not detrimental to health; to provide immediate medical and/or nursing care in cases of accident or illness at work.

The number and type of staff required will depend upon the size of the hospital, but the direction of the service should be the responsibility of the occupational health medical adviser who may be employed on a full-time or part-time basis. The day-to-day administration of the service may be delegated to an experienced occupational health sister who should in all professional matters be directly responsible to the occupational health medical adviser.

Such a service must function as an independent unit advising all appropriate departments and individuals on health and environmental problems and catering for the needs of all who work in the hospital service.

CHAPTER THIRTY-THREE

Honoured by the Rcn

SINCE ITS earliest days the College Council has appointed as Vice-Presidents nurse members and eminent non-nursing individuals who have given outstanding service to the work of the College and of the profession. The list of nurse members so honoured is not long, and thereby illustrates the very high standards set by the Council in deciding upon such appointments. The first nurse Vice-Presidents appointed were:

Dame Sidney Browne, G.B.E., R.R.C. and Bar, Hon. D.N. of Leeds, Florence Nightingale Medal.

Dame Sidney was appointed first President of the College of Nursing when the Council, in 1922, decided that this office should be established. Dame Sidney remained President until 1925, but had already served on the College Council from 1917–19, and was again elected to serve in 1927. She was also appointed the first Nurse Honorary Treasurer of the College in 1917, an office she held until 1927. She was appointed a Vice-President in 1926.

Dame Sidney was trained at the Guest Hospital, Dudley, in 1879 and became a staff nurse at St. Bartholomew's Hospital between 1882 and 1883. She became a sister in the Army Nursing Service at the Royal Victoria Hospital, Netley, and went to North Africa to serve in the Army Nursing Service in the Egyptian War of 1884 and the Sudan Campaign of 1885. Subsequently she was Superintendent of Cottonera Hospital, Malta, Curragh Camp, Woolwich, and Aldershot Hospital. Dame Sidney later went to the Boer War between 1898 and 1902 but was recalled to the War Office to organize Queen Alexandra's Imperial Military Nursing Service of which she was appointed the first Matron-in-Chief (1902–06). Thereafter she became Matron-in-Chief of the Territorial Army Nursing

Service from 1907 to 1919, serving through the First World War and being mentioned twice in dispatches. Dame Sidney died at the great age of ninety-one in 1941, having devoted over forty years of her life to the welfare and progress of the nursing services. By her desire her medals were presented to the College of Nursing—the Royal Red Cross and Bar, Egyptian Medal and Bar, Khedive Star, Queen's Medal, and King's Medal.

After her retirement in 1920 she contributed to *The Times History of the War* and *Cassell's History of Nursing*.

Dame Sarah Swift, G.B.E., R.R.C., Florence Nightingale Medal.

Dame Sarah was the first Member of the College of Nursing and President from 1925 to 1928; Hon. Treasurer 1927–37; Member of the Council 1916–37; appointed Vice-President 1928. Dame Sarah's career and her work in founding the College of Nursing are detailed on pages 25–27 of this work.

Miss Annie Warren Gill, C.B.E., R.R.C. (South African War) and Bar (First World War).

Founder Member of the College of Nursing; Member of the College Council 1916–26 and 1928–30; President of the College 1927–28, and appointed a Vice-President in 1928.

Miss Gill who trained at the Royal Infirmary, Edinburgh, went to the South African War in 1898 and did duty in a concentration camp. Subsequently she was appointed Matron of the Royal Berkshire Hospital, and later Lady Superintendent of her own training hospital, the Royal Infirmary, Edinburgh, from 1907 to 1925. During the First World War she was Principal Matron, Territorial Army Nursing Service, 2nd Scottish General Hospital, from 1914 to 1918.

Miss Gill was a prime mover in the founding of the Scottish Board of the College in 1916 and was its first Hon. Secretary and Hon. Treasurer.

Dame Maud McCarthy, G.B.E., R.R.C. (South African War) and Bar, Queen's Medal and King's Medal (South African War), Legion of Honour (Chevalier), Lady of Grace of the Order of St. John of Jerusalem, Medaille de la Reine Elizabeth avec Croix Rouge (Belgium), Medaille Epidemies en Vermeille, American Red Cross Medal, Florence Nightingale Medal.

Founder Member of the College of Nursing, she served as a Member of the College Council from 1924 to 1929 and was appointed a Vice-President in 1929.

Dame Maud trained at the London Hospital between 1891 and 1893, and served in the Army Nursing Service in the South African War, 1899–1902. She was Matron of the Queen Alexandra's Imperial Military Nursing Service from 1903 to 1910; Principal Matron of the Q.A.I.M.N.S., War Office, from 1910 to 1914; Matron-in-Chief with the British Armies in France from 1914 to 1919; and Matron-in-Chief of the Territorial Army Nursing Service from 1920 to 1925. She was closely concerned with the formation of the Q.A.I.M.N.S., and in the First World War went to France in the first ship to leave England carrying the spearhead of the British Expeditionary Force.

Dame Alicia Lloyd Still, D.B.E., R.R.C., Florence Nightingale Medal, Medaille d'honneur de l'Assistance Publique, Lady of Grace of the Order of St. John of Jerusalem.

Founder Member of the College of Nursing; Member of the College Council 1920–38; and Vice-President 1938.

Details of Dame Alicia's work in the founding of the College and in her own career appear in this history on pages 31–32. One of the most striking personalities of the nursing profession, she was first President of the Association of Hospital Matrons and Matron in her own training school at St. Thomas's Hospital for nearly twenty-five years. Dame Alicia was a member of the first General Nursing Council for England and Wales. She was a member of the Q.A.I.M.N.S. Board and the Army Nursing Service Committee; President of the International Council of Nurses from 1933 to 1937; on her retirement in 1937, was invited to become one of the Governors of St. Thomas's Hospital.

Mrs. Edith MacGregor Rome (née Sheriff-MacGregor), R.R.C., Order of Marie Regina of Roumania 1st Class, Order of St. Anne of Russia.

Member of the College Council, 1931–38; President of the College, 1933–34, and 1937–38 (the first former member of the College Staff to become President). Vice-President 1938.

Mrs. Rome trained at the Westminster Hospital between 1894 and 1898; was Assistant Matron, Warneford Hospital, Leamington Spa, 1898–99; Home Sister, Victoria Hospital, Chelsea, 1899–1905; and Matron of the Children's Hospital, Paddington, 1905–16. From 1916 to 1919 she served in Roumania, Russia, and Serbia with Lady Muriel Paget's Nursing Unit.

Mrs. Rome was Organizing Secretary of the Local Centres from 1920 to 1925, and then the first Secretary of the Student Nurses Association from 1926 to 1930, retiring on her marriage in the latter year. She was a Founder Member of the College and was untiring in her work of establishing the Student Nurses Association. Mrs. Rome was also Matron-in-Chief of the British Red Cross Society from 1935 to 1938.

Dame Ellen Mary Musson, D.B.E., R.R.C., LL.D. Leeds Univ., Florence Nightingale Medal.

A Founder Member of the College and a Member of the College Council from 1916 to 1939, and Nurse Hon. Treasurer, 1938–50. Dame Ellen was the first Nurse Chairman of the General Nursing Council, an office she held from 1926 to 1944.

Dame Ellen trained at St. Bartholomew's Hospital between 1895 and 1898 and thereafter became successively Ward Sister, Night Superintendent, and Assistant Matron at that Hospital. She was Matron of Swansea General and Eye Hospital from 1906 to 1909, and Matron of the General Hospital, Birmingham from 1909 to 1923. Between 1925 and 1947 she was Hon. Treasurer of the International Council of Nurses and became President of the National Council of Nurses in 1945. Her great professional knowledge and legal attitude of mind made her an outstanding figure in the nursing profession of her generation. She accepted a Vice-Presidency of the Royal College of Nursing in 1950.

It has been said in earlier pages that the period of the founding of the College was an age of giants in the nursing profession. Of the great women here listed Dame Ellen Musson lived to the age of ninety-three, Dame Sidney Browne to ninety-one, Dame Maud McCarthy to ninety, and Dame Sarah Swift to eighty-five.

None of the Vice-Presidents named in the foregoing list lived to see the final amalgamation of the Royal College of Nursing with the National Council of Nurses in 1963, although all at various times had urged the union and worked towards that end. After the amalgamation, however, the Council of the joint body decided to create a new appointment for which only nurse members should be eligible—this was Life-Vice-President.

The five appointed at that time were:

Miss Dorothy Sandys Coode, O.B.E.

President of the College from 1935 to 1937; Vice-Chairman of the College Council, 1937–40; Chairman of the College Council, 1940–46. Miss Coode was appointed a Vice-President in 1953.

Trained at the Nightingale School, St. Thomas's Hospital between 1899 and 1902, Miss Coode became Sister-in-Charge at the School between 1903 and 1910 when she was forced to retire through ill health. She was happily able to resume duty in 1913 as Sister-in-Charge at the Preliminary Training School at St. Thomas's Hospital, remaining in that position until 1924 when she was appointed Assistant Matron of the hospital. This post she held until her retirement in 1933.

Upon the outbreak of war in 1939 Miss Coode at once returned to St. Thomas's Hospital, continuing duty through the worst of the enemy air raids in which the hospital was very heavily damaged.

Miss Helen Dey, C.B.E., R.R.C.

Miss Dey was a member of the College Council from 1930 to 1953 when she was elected Nurse Hon. Treasurer, an office she held until 1959.

Helen Dey trained at St. Bartholomew's Hospital. Throughout the First World War she served in Queen Alexandra's Imperial Military Nursing Service and subsequently was appointed to a post at the Detroit Receiving Hospital in America. In 1959 the College Council appointed her a Vice-President and in 1963 a Life-Vice-President.

Helen Dey fought untiringly for the advancement of the nursing profession, in particular for improvement in the socio-economic position of the nurse. With her astute brain and forceful character she was an outstanding Hon. Treasurer of the College over whose finances she was a zealous guardian.

Mrs. Ada Anna Woodman, C.B.E.

A founder member of the College, Mrs. Woodman trained at the Infirmary, Newport, Monmouth, where she was successively Staff Nurse, Sister, and Assistant Matron. Subsequently she became a health visitor and later Superintendent Health Visitor for the County Borough of East Ham.

Mrs. Woodman was elected to the Council of the College in 1941, became Vice-Chairman of the Council in 1946 and Chairman of Council in 1949, an office which she held until 1961, and was appointed a Life-Vice-President in 1963. Mrs. Woodman made an outstanding contribution to the College and the profession during the difficult years following the introduction of the National Health Service. A born negotiator, she served for many years as a College representative on the Staff side of the Whitley Council. Her wisdom, human understanding, and appreciation of nurses' problems, will long be remembered with affection and gratitude by members of the College.

Miss Frances Gowland Goodall, C.B.E.

Secretary and later General Secretary of the Royal College of Nursing from 1933 to 1957. One of the most outstanding figures in College history, Frances Goodall was a brilliant negotiator, committee secretary, and chairman. Details of her career appear on pages 113–114 of this work.

Miss Mary Cochrane, R.R.C.

Honorary Secretary of the National Council of Nurses from 1945 until the amalgamation of that body with the Royal College of Nursing in 1963, when she was appointed a Life-Vice-President of the joint body.

Miss Cochrane trained at Charing Cross Hospital, starting in 1914, and subsequently was Matron of the Hospital from 1924 to 1943. Miss Cochrane, who was also for some years

President of the Royal British Nurses Association, gave devoted service to the National Council. Not only a distinguished member of the nursing profession, she was also a great character, loved and respected by even those who disagreed strenuously with her views which she always held firmly and expressed in unequivocal terms.

Miss Mabel G. Lawson, O.B.E., M.A., M.B., Ch.B.

Mabel Lawson is a unique personality in that at various times she has been engaged not only in most branches of nursing but also in medicine. She qualified as a Bachelor of Medicine at Aberdeen University (graduating in Arts at the same time) and practised medicine for nine years before qualifying as a State Registered Nurse at the Nightingale Training School.

She travelled extensively abroad as a lecturer, observer, and adviser on nursing education and organization on behalf of the Government and the British Council and played a prominent part in the affairs of the International Council of Nurses. A wise, sympathetic, and patient counsellor, Mabel Lawson was one of the chief architects of the amalgamation between the National Council of Nurses and the Royal College of Nursing. She was President of both the National Council and the amalgamated body as well as serving for many years on the General Nursing Council.

BIBLIOGRAPHY

The Order of the Hospital of St John of Jerusalem. W. K. R. Bedford and R. Holbeche. Robinson. London. 1902.

The History of the British Red Cross. S. H. Best. Cassell. London. 1938.

State Registration for Nurses. L. C. Boyd. 1911.

General History of Nursing. L. R. Seymer, M.A., S.R.N. Faber and Faber. London. 1932.

L'Hotel-Dieu de Paris et les Soeurs Augustines. Champion. Paris. 1901.

Mediaeval Hospitals of England. R. M. Clay. Methuen. London. 1909.

The Story of the Growth of Nursing. Agnes E. Pavey, S.R.N. Faber and Faber. London. 1938.

The Birth of Industrial Nursing. I. H. Charley. Belliere Tindall and Cox. London. 1954.

Un Souvenir de Solferino. J. H. Dunant. Cherbuilez. Geneva. 1862.

The Romance of the British Voluntary Hospital Movement. A. D. Evans and L. G. R. Howard. Hutchinson. London. 1930.

A History of the Nursing Profession. Brian Abel-Smith. Heinemann. London. 1960.

A History of Medicine. D. Guthrie. Nelson. London. 1945.

A Hundred Years of Army Nurses. Ian Hay. Cassell. London. 1953.

Inter-departmental Committee on Nursing Services. Report 1939. London. H.M. Stationery Office.

Report of *The Lancet* Commission on Nursing. *The Lancet.* London. 1932.

Nursing Reconstruction Committee Report and Supplement. Rcn. London. 1942.

Life of Florence Nightingale. R. Nash. Macmillan. London. 1925.

William Rathbone; a memoir. E. F. Rathbone. Macmillan. London. 1905.

Administering the Hospital Nursing Service. Rcn. London. 1964.

A Reform of Nursing Education. Rcn. London. 1964.

Appendices

PRESIDENTS OF THE COLLEGE

(The first President was appointed in 1922)

1922–1923	Dame Sidney Browne, G.B.E., R.R.C.
1923–1925	Dame Sidney Browne, G.B.E., R.R.C.
1925–1927	Dame Sarah Swift, G.B.E., R.R.C.
1927–1929	Miss A. W. Gill, R.R.C.
1929–1930	Miss R. Cox-Davies, C.B.E., R.R.C.
1930–1933	Miss M. E. Sparshott, C.B.E., R.R.C.
1933–1934	Mrs. E. MacGregor Rome, R.R.C.
1934–1935	Miss R. Cox-Davies, C.B.E., R.R.C.
1935–1937	Miss D. S. Coode, O.B.E.
1937–1938	Mrs. E. MacGregor Rome, R.R.C.
1938–1940	Miss B. M. Monk, C.B.E., R.R.C.
1940–1942	Miss M. Jones, O.B.E., A.R.R.C.
1942–1944	Miss E. E. P. MacManus, O.B.E.
1944–1946	Miss M. F. Hughes
1946–1948	Miss G. V. L. Hillyers, O.B.E.
1948–1950	Dame Louisa Wilkinson, D.B.E., R.R.C.
1950–1952	Miss L. G. Duff Grant, R.R.C.
1952–1954	Miss L. J. Ottley
1954–1956	Miss S. C. Bovill
1956–1958	Miss G. M. Godden, O.B.E.
1958–1960	Miss M. J. Marriott, O.B.E.
1960–1962	Miss M. J. Smyth, C.B.E.
1962–1963	Miss M. J. Marriott, O.B.E.
1963–1964	Miss M. G. Lawson, O.B.E.
1964–1966	Miss F. N. Udell, C.B.E.
1966–	Miss T. Turner, O.B.E., A.R.R.C.

CHAIRMEN OF THE COUNCIL

1916–1940 The Hon. Sir Arthur Stanley, G.B.E., C.B., M.V.O., LL.D.
1940–1946 Miss D. S. Coode, O.B.E.
1946–1947 Miss B. M. Monk, C.B.E., R.R.C.
1947–1949 Miss M. F. Hughes
1949–1961 Mrs. A. A. Woodman, C.B.E.
1961–1964 Miss E. M. Rees
1964–1966 Miss M. Blakeley
1966– Miss S. M. Collins

SECRETARIES OF THE COLLEGE

1916–1933 Miss Mary S. Rundle, R.R.C., Secretary
1933–1957 Miss Frances G. Goodall, C.B.E., General Secretary
1957– Miss Catherine M. Hall, General Secretary

FIRST COUNCIL

The first meeting of the Council of the College of Nursing Ltd. was held on 1 April 1916 at 83 Pall Mall (The Royal Automobile Club) which was also its first registered office.

The membership of the Council as appointed by the signatories to the articles of association was:

Miss R. Cox-Davies, R.R.C., Matron, Royal Free Hospital.

Miss A. Lloyd Still, C.B.E., R.R.C., Matron, St. Thomas's Hospital.

Miss S. A. Swift, R.R.C., Matron-in-Chief, Joint War Committee, British Red Cross Society and Order of St. John of Jerusalem.

Miss J. Melrose, R.R.C., Matron, Royal Infirmary, Glasgow.

Miss A. Hughes, late General Inspector, Q.V.J.N.I. Nurses.

Miss Jane Walker, M.D.

Miss L. V. Haughton, Matron, Guy's Hospital.

Miss M. E. Ray, R.R.C., Matron, King's College Hospital.

Miss A. W. Gill, R.R.C., Lady Superintendent, Royal Infirmary, Edinburgh.

Miss A. B. Baillie, R.R.C., Matron, Royal Infirmary, Bristol.

Miss M. E. Sparshott, R.R.C., Lady Superintendent, Royal Infirmary, Manchester.

The Hon. Arthur Stanley, M.P., M.V.O.

Sir Cooper Perry, M.D., F.R.C.P.

Mr. Comyns Berkeley, M.C., M.A., M.D., F.R.C.P. (later Hon. Treasurer).

Dr. H. G. Turney, F.R.C.P.

Col. James Cantlie, F.R.C.S.

Miss A. C. Gibson, Matron, The Infirmary, Birmingham.

Mr. W. Minet, Governor of St. Thomas's Hospital.

The First Council was appointed but, from 1918 onward, one third of the members thereof retired. Elections to the Council were held in 1918–1919–1920 so that the first fully-elected Council took office in 1920.

The Hon. Arthur Stanley was elected Chairman and Sir Cooper Perry temporary Hon. Secretary. The Council co-opted the following extra members:

Miss E. Barton, R.R.C., Matron, Chelsea Infirmary.

Prof. J. Glaister, M.D., University of Glasgow.

Miss A. McIntosh, C.B.E., R.R.C., Matron, St. Bartholomew's Hospital.

Miss E. Mowat, Matron, Whitechapel Infirmary.

Miss E. M. Musson, R.R.C., Matron, Birmingham General Hospital.

Miss C. E. Vincent, R.R.C., Lady Superintendent, Royal Infirmary, Leicester.

Miss Seymour Yapp, Superintendent Nurse, Ashton-Under-Lyne Infirmary.

At the third meeting of the College Council held on 20 April of the same year, the Consultative Committee, the Examination Committee, the College Registration Committee, the Establishment and General Purposes Committee, and the Finance Committee were formed.

At the fourth meeting on the following 4 May it was announced that the application of Miss Mary Rundle for the post of Secretary to the College had been accepted.

The first Ordinary General Meeting of the College of Nursing Ltd. was held at the registered offices on the 18th of the same month. Mr. Stanley, the Chairman, presented the first Annual Report, which included a balance sheet drawn up by the Hon. Treasurer, Comyns Berkeley, showing the following donations:

J. D. Cohn, Esq. £200 0 0
Miss S. Yapp 5 5 0
'A Poor-Law Medical Officer'   .   .   .   1 1 0

After making deductions for solicitors' and registration fees,
salary of a temporary clerk, printing, postage, stationery, etc., the
newly-launched College of Nursing had a bank balance of some
pence over £16.

Other donations which did not appear in the first report were
the free use of rooms including lighting and heating at Vere Street
given by Col. (later Sir) James Cantlie, and Mr. (later Sir) William
Boyton, M.P.

Index

Aberdeen University, 167
Addison, Dr. Christopher, 56, 65
Administering Hospital Nursing Service (1964) Report, 182
Admiralty, 76
Airlie, Dowager Countess of, 79
Albert Hall Mass Meeting, 174
American Nurses, Congress of, 144
Anniversary, Twenty-first, 96
Appointments Bureau, 75, 77
Area Organisers, 96
Arms, Grant of, 97
Articles of Association, 34, 35, 45
Asquith, Cyril, 94
Assistant Nurses, 110, 113, 117, 122, 127, 164
Athlone Committee, 108, 111, 113, 114, 116, 118, 127, 130
Athlone, Earl of, 107
Attendants upon the Chronic Sick, 110

Baillie, Miss A. B., R.R.C., 197
Banks, Mitchell, K.C., 94
Bartholomew's (St.) Hospital, 1, 19, 30, 37
Barton, Miss E., R.R.C., 198
Bedford College, 91, 98
Bedford Fenwick, Dr., 2
Bedford Fenwick, Mrs. Ethel, 3, 4, 5-7, 9, 15, 21-23, 27, 28, 36, 40-44, 49, 50, 52, 54, 55, 58, 59, 61, 66, 73, 81, 117, 142-144, 165, 167
Belfast Centre, 91
Benedict (Saint), 8
Berkeley, Comyns, 32, 34, 198
Bevan, Aneurin, M.P., 131, 135-40, 152
Birmingham Centre, 102
Blakeley, Miss M., 197
Bonchurch Rest Home, 70
Boulton, Capt. Harold, 45

Bovill, Miss S. C., 196
Boyton, William, 199
Branches, 89
Bridgeman, Walter, 45
British College of Nurses, 81
British Journal of Nursing, 58, 59, 66, 73, 74
British Nurses Association (*also see* R.B.N.A.) 2
British Red Cross, 11, 23, 25, 26, 35
British Women's Hospital Committee 69
Brockway, Fenner, 107
Brompton Hospital, 31
Browne, Dame Sidney, G.B.E., R.R.C., 80, 188, 196
Brownlow Hill Parish Infirmary, 13
Brunton, Mary A., 37
Bulletin, Quarterly, 68, 77, 89
Bunsen, Sir Maurice de, 94
Burgess, Miss, 71

Canterbury, Archbishop of, 79
Cantlie, Col. James, 198, 199
Carnegie United Kingdom Trust, 39
Carpenter, Mary F., 102
Cassell, Sir Ernest, G.C.B., 44
Central Health Services Council (Standing Nursing Advisory Committee), 1948, 152-60
Central Home and Training School for Nurses, 15
Central Midwives Board, 7, 32
Chelsea Hospital for Women, 32
Chicago World Fair, 6
Christian Science Attendants, 128
Churchill, Winston, 129
City of London Lying In Hospital 32
Civil Nursing Reserve, 100, 120, 127
Clinical Nursing Officer, 183
Cochrane, Miss Mary, R.R.C., 193
Cohen, Dr., 142